TI-83 Plus Companion

Marla M. Bell

Kennesaw State University

to accompany

Elementary Statistics

Ninth Edition

and

Elementary Statistics Using Excel®

Second Edition

Mario F. Triola

Dutchess Community College

PEARSON

Addison
Wesley

Boston   San Francisco   New York
London   Toronto   Sydney   Tokyo   Singapore   Madrid
Mexico City   Munich   Paris   Cape Town   Hong Kong   Montreal

Contents

Preface

The TI-83 Plus is a wonderful tool to aid in the study and implementation of statistics. It has many built-in features especially for the practice of statistics, features which this companion will introduce and explain. The TI-83 calculator works like the TI-83 Plus for most procedures. Differences between the two will be pointed out. This companion is designed to be used side-by-side with the text *Elementary Statistics (9th Edition)* by Mario F. Triola. As an example, Chapter 2 of the text introduces frequency tables. It describes various types of frequency tables and uses an example based on a data set in Appendix B of the text. This companion uses the <u>same</u> example as the text to illustrate how the TI-83 Plus can be used to make the various types of frequency tables.

This companion follows the text of *Elementary Statistics* chapter by chapter offering TI-83 Plus techniques for most topics. The examples used are directly from the text. These examples are often paraphrased for the sake of brevity, but should be recognizable enough to the reader. The reader is urged to consult the text for important details such as definitions, requirements for running a procedure, and detailed conclusions in context.

Chapters 1 and 2 are very important for your understanding of all the other chapters in this companion. Chapter 1 introduces you to the TI-83 Plus keyboard and to some skills which you will need often, such as saving and deleting data. Chapter 2 introduces you to the TI-83 Plus capabilities in descriptive statistics.

There are undoubtedly a variety of ways to perform the operations described in this companion. In most cases, I have chosen to present only one way of doing everything.

I have chosen to show exact key strokes for all instructions. I strongly urge you to look at all times at what you are pressing and the result. If you hurriedly press a sequence of five or six buttons without paying attention, you will get the desired result, but it will be hard for you to duplicate on your own because you will not see the logic behind the key choices. It is valuable for you to know where things are located on the TI-83 Plus menus. The back inside cover of this companion has a "TI-83 Plus Quick Reference" that summarizes some important keys, menus, and functions used in this companion.

Real data sets are used throughout the main text and are provided in printed form in Appendix B of the main text. These can be installed on your TI-83 Plus from another TI-83 Plus or from a computer. See the Appendix of this companion for details.

I wish to thank Mario F. Triola, without whom this companion would not be possible. I also wish to thank the many students who have taken my statistics courses over the past nine years at Kennesaw State University. Thanks also to Christine O'Brien and Joe Vetere of Addison Wesley for their patience and assistance.

1   Introduction to Statistics (and the TI-83 Plus)

In this chapter we introduce our calculator companion to Triola's *Elementary Statistics* (9th ed.) by giving an overview of the TI-83 Plus keyboard. Read this section carefully in order to familiarize yourself with the keys and menus most utilized in this manual

You will also learn how to set the correct MODE on the TI-83 Plus to ensure that you will obtain the same results as this companion does. You will learn other useful skills such as adjusting the screen contrast and checking the battery strength

Aside from the above technical skills, you will learn some basic skills that are particularly useful throughout your study of Triola's *Elementary Statistics*. Throughout this companion, we will present the uses of the TI-83 Plus by illustrating its use on actual textbook examples. The first will be an exercise from the text which requires the selection of a random sample. There are not many calculator exercises in Chapter 1 of your textbook because it is an overview and introduction chapter. We will take the opportunity in Chapter 1 of this companion to introduce you to skills which you will find necessary throughout the other chapters. These skills include Home screen calculations and saving and editing lists of data in the STAT editor.

KEYBOARD AND NOTATION

The TI-83 Plus keyboard has 5 columns and 10 rows of keys. This may seem like a lot, but the best way to familiarize yourself with the keyboard is to actually work with the calculator and learn out of necessity. You will find the following keys among the most useful and thus they are found in prominent positions on the keyboard.

- The cursor control keys ◀, ▶, ▲ and ▼ are located toward the upper right of your keyboard. These keys allow you to move the cursor on your screen in the direction which the arrow indicates.
- The Y= key is in the upper left of the keyboard. It is utilized more in other types of mathematics courses (such as algebra) than in a statistics course; however you will use the *yellow 2nd* function above it quite often. This is the STAT PLOT menu. We will discuss the yellow 2nd functions shortly.
- The ON key is in the bottom left of the keyboard. Its function is self-explanatory.
- The ENTER key is in the bottom right of the keyboard. You will often need to press this key in order to have the calculator actually do what you have instructed it to do with your preceding keystrokes.
- The GRAPH key is in the upper right of the keyboard.

As mentioned briefly above, most keys on the keyboard have more than one function. The primary function is marked on the key itself and the alternative functions are marked in yellow and green above the key. Below you will be instructed on how to engage the functions which appear in yellow or green.

The Yellow [2nd] Key

If you wish to engage a function which appears in yellow above a key, you must first press the [2nd] key. This key is the only key on the keyboard which is itself yellow, and it is located near the upper left of the keyboard just under the [Y=] key. You will know the second key is engaged when the cursor on your screen changes to a blinking ⬆.
As an example if you wish to call the STAT PLOTS menu which is in yellow above the [Y=] key, you will press [2nd] [Y=].

The Green [ALPHA] Key

You will note that the values appearing in green above keys are mostly letters of the alphabet. This is because there are some situations in which you will wish to name variables or lists and in doing so you will need to type the letters or names. If you wish to type a letter on the screen you must first press the [ALPHA] key. This key is the only key which appears in green. It is directly under the [2nd] key. You will know the [ALPHA] key has been engaged when the cursor on the screen turns into a blinking ⓐ. After pressing the [ALPHA] key you should press the key above which your letter appears in green. As an example if you wish to type the letter E, press [ALPHA] [SIN] (because E is above [SIN].)
Note: If you have a sequence of letters to type, you will want to press [2nd] [ALPHA]. This will engage the yellow function above the [ALPHA] key which is the A-LOCK function. It locks the calculator into the Alpha mode, so that you can repeatedly press keys and get the green function for each. Otherwise, you would have to press [ALPHA] before each choice. Press [ALPHA] again to release the calculator from the A-LOCK mode.

Some General Keyboard Patterns and Important Keys
1. The top row is for plotting and graphing.
2. The second row down has the important yellow QUIT function ([2nd] [MODE]). It also contains the keys useful for editing ([DEL], [2nd] [DEL] (INS), ◀, ▶, ▲ and ▼).
3. The [MATH] key in the first column leads to a set of menus of mathematical functions. Several other mathematical functions (like x^2) have keys in the first column.
4. The keys for arithmetic operations are in the last column ([÷] [×] [−] [+]).
   Note: On the TI-83 Plus screen, the [÷] shows as /, and the [×] shows as *.
5. The [STAT] key, the [VARS] key and the second yellow functions associated with each are central to our study of statistics and probability. (Locate these keys now!)
6. The [,] key is located in the sixth row directly above the [7] key. It is used quite often for grouping and spacing.
7. The [STO▶] key is used for storing values. It is located near the bottom left of the keyboard directly above the [ON] key. It appears as a ➔ on the display screen.

8. The $(-)$ key on the bottom row (to the left of $\boxed{\text{ENTER}}$) is the key used to denote <u>negative</u> numbers. It differs from the subtraction key $\boxed{-}$.

Note: The $(-)$ shows as ⁻ on the screen, smaller and higher than the subtraction sign.

SETTING THE CORRECT MODE

If your answers do not show as many decimal places as the ones shown in this companion or if you have difficulty matching any other output, check your MODE settings. Below we instruct on setting the best MODE settings for our work. These are the ones we have used throughout this companion.

Press the $\boxed{\text{MODE}}$ key (in the second row, second column). You should see a screen like the one on the right. If your calculator has been used previously by you or someone else the highlighted choices may differ. If your screen does have different highlighted choices use the $\boxed{\blacktriangle}$ and $\boxed{\blacktriangledown}$ keys to go to each row with a different choice and press $\boxed{\text{ENTER}}$ when the cursor is on the first choice in each row. This will highlight the first choice in each row. Continue until your screen looks exactly like screen (1) at the right.

Press $\boxed{\text{2nd}}$ $\boxed{\text{MODE}}$ (QUIT) to return to the Home Screen.

(1)

SCREEN CONTRAST ADJUSTMENT AND BATTERY CHECK

To adjust the screen contrast follow these steps:

To increase the contrast, press and release the $\boxed{\text{2nd}}$ key and hold down the $\boxed{\blacktriangle}$ key. You will see the contrast increasing. There will be a number in the upper-left corner of the screen which increases from 0 (lightest) to 9 (darkest).

To decrease the contrast, press and release the $\boxed{\text{2nd}}$ key and hold down the $\boxed{\blacktriangledown}$ key. You will see the contrast decreasing. The number in the upper-left corner of the screen will decrease as you hold. The lightest setting may appear as a blank screen. If this occurs, simply follow the instructions for increasing the contrast, and your display will reappear.

When the batteries are low, the display begins to dim (especially during calculations) and you must adjust to a higher contrast setting than you normally use. If you have to set the contrast setting to 9, you will soon need to replace the four AAA batteries. Your calculator will display a low-battery message to warn you when it is time. After you change batteries, you will need to readjust your contrast as explained above.

Note: It is important to turn off your calculator and change the batteries as soon as you see the "low battery" message in order to avoid loss of your data or corruption of calculator memory.

RANDOM SAMPLES

EXAMPLE: Random Sample and Simple Random Sample (modified for calculator).
Picture a classroom with 60 students arranged in six rows of 10 students each. Use the TI 83 Plus to simulate the results when a sample of 10 students is chosen as follows:
a) The professor will roll a six-sided die in order to choose a row. The students in that row are the sample.
b) The professor will choose a *simple random sample* of 10 students from the class.

1. Press [ON] to turn the calculator on. A cursor should be blinking on the Home screen. If not, press [2nd] [MODE] to Quit and return to the Home screen.

2. Press the [CLEAR] key if the cursor is not in the upper left corner.

3. We will first answer the a) question by simulating the roll of a six-sided die. This means we need to generate a random integer between 1 and 6. The TI-83 Plus has a random number generator built into it. Such programs are dependent upon a value known as the "seed". The calculator comes with a preset value for the seed, but we can reset the value. In this companion, we reset the seed each time we are generating a random sample, so that your output will match that in the companion. In normal practice, you do not need to reset the seed. Let us set the seed this time as follows:
   a) On the Home screen type 123. Then press [STO▸] [MATH] [◀]. Watch what is happening – You went to the Math <PRB> menu. Look at option 1. It is "rand". You should see screen (2).
   b) Now press [1] and you will see that "rand" is pasted at the top of the Home screen as in screen (3).
   c) Press [ENTER] and you will see the 123 as on the second line of screen (3). This indicates the seed is now set.

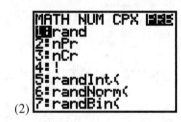

(2)

4. We will now simulate a single roll of a six-sided die by asking for a random integer between 1 and 6. Do so by pressing [MATH] [◀] [5] (thus choosing the option "randInt" off of the Math <PRB> menu). Type 1,6 (remember the [,] key is above the [7]). Press [ENTER] to see the rest of screen (3). We see the result is a 5, so the students in row 5 would be chosen.

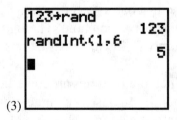

(3)

5. Next we tackle question b). We want a simple random sample of 10 of the 60 students. First number the students (1 to 60). Now you need a random sample of 10 integers between 1 and 60. This time we set the seed as 222. (This is only

necessary if you wish to replicate our results.) Press
MATH ◄ 5 .. Type 1,60,10. Press ENTER. You should
see screen (4). We cannot see all 10 numbers.
You can use the ► key to move across and see the ones
which are not displayed. Note that the 10 we typed
indicated we wanted a sample of size 10.

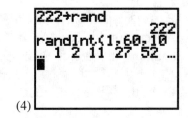

(4)

In the above example, students 31, 1, 2, 11, 27, 52, 47, 4, 15, and 46 were chosen. It is
possible that a student's number could have come up twice in the sample. If this occurs in a
setting where this is not allowed (as in this one) then simply generate some more numbers
until you have the desired sample size.

HOME SCREEN CALCULATIONS AND STORING RESULTS

CUMULATIVE REVIEW EXERCISES: Calculator Warm-ups

We will use exercises 2 and 5 to illustrate some techniques. Afterward we supply solutions
to the other exercises, so you can practice with the techniques.

Exercise 2: $\dfrac{98.20 - 98.60}{0.62}$

We will calculate the value in two ways. In doing so, we will intentionally make a mistake
to show you how to correct errors using the DEL key. We will also discuss the "Ans" and
"Last Entry" features.

1. Type 98.20 – 97..60 (an intentional mistake)

2. To correct the mistakes use the ◄ cursor key to
    move backward until your cursor is blinking on one
    of the double decimal points as shown in screen (5).
    Press DEL and the duplicate decimal point will be
    deleted. Now press ◄ until the cursor is blinking on
    the 7. Type an 8, and it will replace the incorrect 7.
    Press ENTER for the numerator difference of ⁻4 as
    shown in the top of screen (6).

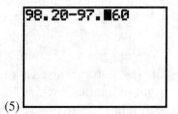

(5)

3. Press ÷. (Note that "Ans/" appears on the screen).
    Type 0.62 and press ENTER for the result of ⁻.645.
    Note: "Ans" represents the last result of a calculation which
    was displayed alone and right-justified on the Home screen.
    Pressing ÷ without first typing a value called for something to
    be divided, so "Ans" was supplied.

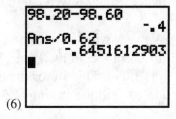

(6)

4. Press [2nd] [ENTER]. This calls the "last entry" to the screen. (in this case Ans/0.62). Press [2nd] [ENTER] again to get back to 98.20-98.60.

5. Press the [▲] key to move to the front of the line.

6. Press [2nd] [DEL] (for INS). You will see a blinking underline cursor. Type [(] to insert a left parenthesis before the first 9.

7. Press [▼] to jump to the end of the line. Type [)] [÷] 0.62 to see screen (7). Press [ENTER] for the same result as before.

Exercise 5 $\sqrt{\dfrac{(5-7)^2 + (12-7)^2 + (4-7)^2}{3-1}}$

In this example, we will use the ANS Yellow Key, illustrate syntax errors and show how to store quantities using variable names.

1. Type (5-7)^2+(12-7)^2+(4-7)^2 as in screen (8). Press [ENTER] for the value 38. (Use the [x²] key for the ^{2})

2. Press [2nd] [x²] [2nd] [(-)] [÷] and then type (3-1). Press [ENTER] for the desired results at the bottom of screen (8). Note that the [2nd] [x²] sequence is the $\sqrt{}$ function and the [2nd] [(-)] sequence calls the last answer "Ans" back to the screen.

3. In screen (9) we attempt to do the whole exercise in one step. Pressing [ENTER] brings screen (10) because we have made an error. Press 2 to "goto" the error. We get screen (11) which has a blinking cursor on the last parenthesis. This means we have an extra right parenthesis which has no matching left parenthesis. Screen (12) shows the result when we go back and insert the missing left parenthesis into the calculation. We get the same result as before.

4. We now want to store parts of the above problem in different locations. Type (5-7)^2. Press [STO▶] [ALPHA] [×] [ENTER]. This stores the quantity as R. See screen (13). Continue storing (12-7)^2 and (4-7)^2 as S and T.

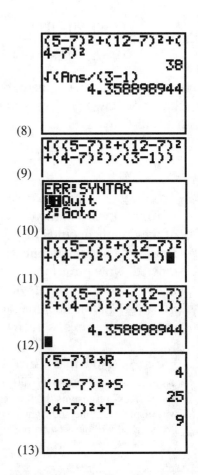

5. In screen (14) we sum R, S and T and store the sum as H. We again get 38 for this sum. We continue by taking the square root of H and dividing by (3-1) as also seen in screen (14). The result is again 4.358898944.

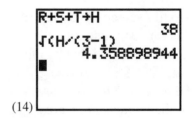

(14)

Following are solutions for the other exercises. These are just suggestions. Alternative solutions are possible.

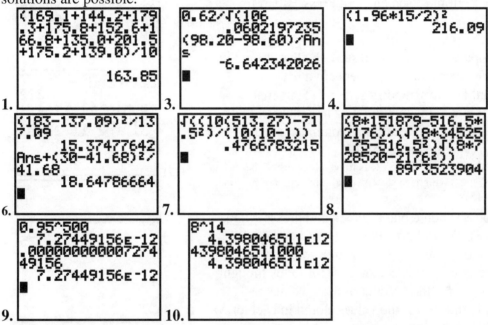

STORING LISTS OF DATA

Your text, like the real world, is full of sets of real data. In order to analyze the data, you must store it in a list in your TI-83 Plus. Here, we will show you how to do this. Additionally, you should know that all of the data sets in the Appendix of your textbook are available to be transferred to your calculator from another calculator (or from a computer). You can then use the APPS key to transfer a set into your lists. See your instructor and/or the Appendix of this companion for more information.

Storing Lists of Data from the Home Screen

EXERCISE: Random Sample of 10 Students: Revisited from pages 4 and 5 of this companion: Ten random integers between 1 and 60 were generated and displayed in a list on screen (4). We will modify the example to store the integers in list L2 on the TI-83 Plus. We will then store the data in a list which we name ourselves.

Modify screen (4) by repeating the first three lines, but this time stipulate that the integers you generate will be stored in L2. Do this by typing [STO▸] [2nd] [2] after the randInt(1,60,10). Press [ENTER] for the top of Screen (15). To recall the list you have stored, so that it all appears on the Home screen press [2nd] [STO▸] [2nd] [2]. (The sequence [2nd] [STO▸] chooses the RCL (or recall) function and [2nd] [2] chooses list L2 as what will be recalled.) See bottom of screen (15). Press [ENTER] for screen (16).

Now let's suppose we decided to store the list of random integers which correspond to students in a list named STU. We would simply modify screen (15) so that instead of L2 we would store the data in a place called STU. See screen (17). Recall that you must use the [ALPHA] key to type the name "STU".

Note: The TI-83 will know that STU is to be a list without being told because you are asking it to store several numbers, not just one.

Try this! Type STU on a blank screen and press [ENTER]. See screen (18). We did not get our list of numbers back. In fact, we got 0. (You may have gotten some other value). The reason for this is that the TI-83 Plus thought we were asking it for the product of three values S, T, and U. See screen (19) for the values stored in each of these places. (Your results may vary). Recall that values for S and T were stored earlier in our work on page 7. So how do we recall our list which we named STU? We must press [2nd] [STAT] for a screen like screen (20). This is your calculators LISTS menu. The names of all lists stored in your calculator will appear in this menu (in alphabetical order). Use your cursor to look down the list of NAMES until you highlight the name STU. Press [ENTER] twice. You should see screen (21). You will notice that what has been pasted on the Home screen is LSTU and not simply STU.

So while we did not need to specify that STU was a list when we first stored our data, we did need to specify this fact when we were trying to recall it. In situations where it is unclear whether or not you need the small L in front of the name of a list, your safest bet is to paste the name in from the LISTS <NAMES> menu as we did above.

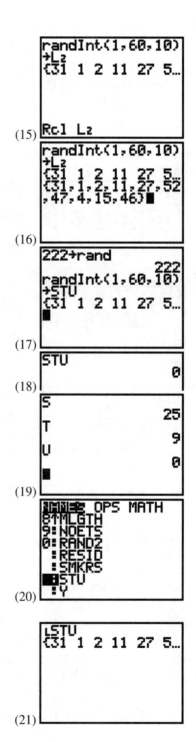

(15)

(16)

(17)

(18)

(19)

(20)

(21)

Storing Lists of Data Using the STAT Editor

Using the STAT Editor is the easiest way to store lists and work with the data therein. The STAT Editor comes with 6 lists named L1 through L6. Other lists can be added if desired. The number of lists is only limited by the memory size.

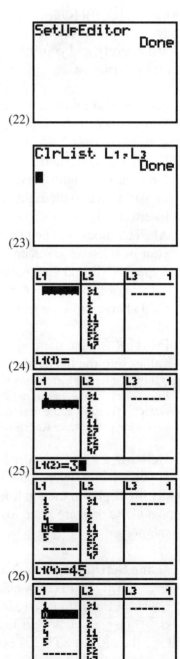

SetUpEditor: If you want the STAT Editor to be restored to its original condition (with lists L1 to L6 only.) Press [STAT] [5] [ENTER]. You will see screen (22). Often students find this necessary because they have inadvertently deleted one of the original lists.

(22)

1. Clearing Lists in the Stat Editor:
   Let's say you want to clear out the contents from lists L1 and L3 before you start a problem. Press [STAT] [4] to choose the ClrList option from the Editor. Then press [2nd] [1] [,] [2nd] [3] to choose your two lists with a comma between them as seen in screen (23). The comma is needed if you are clearing multiple lists at one time as we are here. Press [ENTER] to see the message that it is "Done".

(23)

2. View or Edit in the STAT Editor:
   If you press [STAT] [1] you should see screen (24) with L1 and L3 cleared out and with our 10 random integers still stored in L2.

(24)

3. Entering Data into the STAT Editor:
a) With the cursor at the first row of L1, type 1 and press [ENTER]. The cursor moves down one row.
b) Type 3, and the screen will look like screen (25), with 3 in the bottom line. Press [ENTER] and the 3 will be pasted into the second row of the list.
c) Continue with 4, 45, and 5 as seen in screen (26).

(25)

(26)

4. Correcting Mistakes with DEL and INS:
a) In screen (26) we can delete the 45 by using the [▲] key until it is highlighted and then pressing [DEL].
b) To insert a 2 above the 3 move the cursor to the 3 then press [2nd] [DEL] (to choose the INS or insert mode). You will see screen (27). Note a 0 was inserted where you wanted the 2 to go.
c) Type 2 and press [ENTER] to replace the 0.

(27)

5. Clearing Lists without Leaving the STAT Editor:

Suppose you wish to clear a list, say L2, while you are still in the STAT Editor. You should use the cursor to highlight the name of the list at the top.. With the name highlighted press CLEAR and you will see screen (28). Press ENTER (or ▼) and the contents of the list will be cleared. Make sure not to press DEL or the list will be deleted entirely and you will have to run the SetUp Editor to retrieve it.

6. Storing Data with a Named List:

Suppose we wish to store the 10 random integers found previously (17, 44, 43, 28, 27, 51, 30, 39, 34, and 32) in a list named Rand2.

a. First with L2 highlighted at the top press 2nd DEL. L2 will move to the right and there will be a new list inserted in its place. The calculator will be in ALPHA mode and be prompting you for the name of your new list as in screen (29).

b. Type RAND and then press ALPHA to release the calculator from ALPHA mode, so you can type the final character in the name which is 2. See screen (30).

c. Press ENTER and then ▼. Now input the desired values into the list as in screen (31).

Note: If the list Rand2 had already been created, its name could have been pasted in to screen (29). In either case, if the list already existed its entire contents (if there were any) would have been pasted in as well as its name.

7. Deleting a List from the STAT Editor:

If you wish to delete a list from you STAT Editor, simply highlight on the top line and press DEL. The name and the data are gone from the Editor but not from the memory.

8. Using SetUp Editor to Name a List:

Press STAT 5 to call the SetUp Editor. Now type IDS, STU, L1 as in screen (32). Then press ENTER. Then press STAT 1 to view your lists. As in screen (33) you will see the old list STU has been placed back in full view. Also there is a new list IDS ready and waiting for some data to be entered.

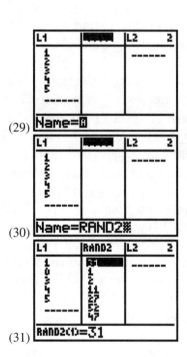

(28)

(29)

(30)

(31)

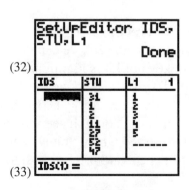

(32)

(33)

9. Making a Copy of a List:

Use cursor control keys to highlight the top of the new list IDS as in screen (34). Press 2nd 1 to paste in the name L1 as in the bottom line of screen (34). Press ENTER and the L1 data appears under IDS. The contents of L1 have been copied to IDS.

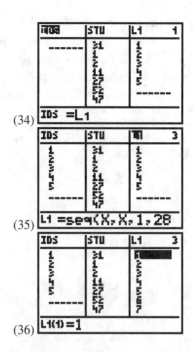

(34)

10. Generating a Sequence of Numbers in a List:

Use cursor control keys to highlight L1 as in the top line in screen (35). Press 2nd STAT ▶ 5. You are choosing the LIST menu and then choosing the OPS submenu. From the OPS submenu you are choosing option 5 which is "seq(". This is pasted onto the bottom line of screen (35). Type in the rest so that you have seq(X,X,1,28. Press ENTER and the sequence of integers from 1 to 28 will be pasted into L1 as in screen (36).

(35)

(36)

Note: To quickly check the values on a multi-screen spreadsheet you can press the green ALPHA key followed by either the ▲ or ▼ key. This will allow you to jump up or down from one page (screen) to another. The green arrows on the keyboard near the ▲ and ▼ keys are there to remind you of this capability.

11. Deleting a Named List from Memory:

a) To remove both the name of a list and its data from RAM press 2nd + to call the MEM function. You should see screen (37).

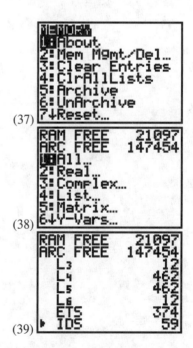

(37)

b) Press 2 to choose Mem Mgmt/Del. You will get a screen like (38).

c) Press 4 to choose to see a display of *List* names. Use ▼ to move down the display to the list you want to remove (say IDS) as shown in screen (39).

(38)

d) Press DEL to delete the list. You can remove lists one by one from this screen.

e) Press 2nd MODE to QUIT and return to the Home screen.

(39)

Note: (For TI-83 Plus only) If the list was also saved in a Group stored in Archive memory, the above procedure has not deleted the copy. (See the Appendix for more information on Groups.) Groups can be deleted from the calculator if in step c) above you replace 4:List… with 8:Group… .

12. Using the Augment Function for Large Lists:

Several lists can be combined into one large list by using an option which is on the LISTS <OPS> submenu at option 9. This is the augment option. For example if you wish to combine lists L1 and L2 and store the combined list in L3, you can press 2nd STAT ▶

9 to paste the "augment(" on your Home screen. Then put the names of the lists you wish to combine on the screen separated by commas. Close the parentheses. Then press STO▶ 2nd 3 to store in L3. Finally press ENTER. This function will only work if there is actually data in the lists you are augmenting.

Note: The "augment" function could be used so that several students could cooperate in typing in a large set of data. Each student could type part of the data set into a different list (L1, L2, L3, etc.) Then the calculators could be linked, the lists transferred to one calculator and then the augment function could be used to combine them into one large list which could then be redistributed for all to share.

2 Describing, Exploring, and Comparing Data

This chapter introduces the graphical plotting and summary statistics capabilities of the TI-83 Plus. First row keys like [2nd] [Y=] (STAT PLOTS) are used to obtain descriptive plots of data sets. Many of the summary statistics of Chapter 2 can be obtained by pressing [STAT] [▶] [1] This gets you the 1-Var Stats option in the Stat <Calc> menu. The author assumes you have read and familiarized yourself with the content of Chapter 1. Based on this assumption, the presentation of subsequent chapters is more abbreviated.

FREQUENCY TABLES

Note: Information on how the TI-83 Plus can aid in construction of frequency tables from raw data is found in the section entitled Histograms and Frequency Tables from Raw Data on page 17.

EXAMPLE [Table 2-2] We will use the data on the cotinine levels of smokers to illustrate the use of the TI-83 Plus in obtaining all types of frequency tables. The frequency table for this data is repeated on the right with the class midpoints included. As illustrated in screen (1), put the midpoints in L1 and the frequencies in L2.

Class Limits Cotinine levels	L1 Midpts.	L2 Freq
0-99	49.5	11
100-199	149.5	12
200-299	249.5	14
300-399	349.5	1
400-499	449.5	2

Relative Frequency Table [Table 2-3]

We calculate relative frequencies in L3 .

1. Highlight L3 at the top of the column as in screen (1).

2. Type L2÷40*100 as in the bottom of screen (1). We use "40" because it is the sum of the frequencies.

3. Press [ENTER]. You should see Screen (2).

Note: We could have used sum(L2) instead of 40 in step 2 with "sum(" pasted in from [2nd] [STAT] <MATH>.

(1)

(2)

Cumulative Frequency Table [Table 2-4]

We calculate cumulative frequencies in L4 .

1. Use ▶ to continue beyond L3 to L4 . Highlight L4 at the top of the column as in Screen (3).

2. Press [2nd] [STAT] [▶] [6] [2nd] [2] to type the ":cumSum(L2 "as in screen (3).

3. Press [ENTER] for Screen (4). We can see from the last row that there were a total of 40 values in this data set.

[Exercises 15-20] These exercises require the creation of frequency tables from raw data. The TI-83 Plus can aid in this process. See the section on Histograms and Frequency Tables from Raw Data.

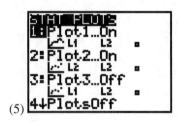
(3)

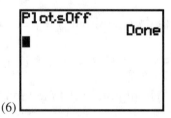
(4)

HISTOGRAMS FROM FREQUENCY TABLES

FIGURE 2-1: We continue with the cotinine level of smokers example. The class midpoints remain in L1 with the frequencies in L2 .

1. **Turning OFF all Stat Plots**
   Activate your Stat Plots by pressing [2nd] [Y=]. You should see a screen somewhat like Screen (5). If all plots are not off, press **4**:PlotsOff and [ENTER]. You should see screen (6).
   Note: If you or anyone else has been using the [Y=] edit screen, it is a good idea to also make sure all plots on this screen are off. You can clear an equation on this screen by moving the cursor to the right of the equal sign and pressing [CLEAR].

(5)

(6)

2. **Turning On and Setting Up Stat Plot1**

   (a) Press [2nd] [Y=] [1] to engage **Stat Plot1**. This gives you a screen, similar to screen (7) on which you will define the properties of the type of plot you will create.
   (b) Use the ▲ and ▼ keys to highlight the choices on screen (7). You must press [ENTER] after each choice to activate it. Notice that we are choosing

(7)

to plot a histogram. It is the third choice in the "Type" row. We specify L1 as the "Xlist' and L2 as the "Freq" which is short for "frequencies".

2. Setting Up Plot Windows.

(a) Press WINDOW. You should see a screen similar to screen (8). (Your numbers will not be the same.) We will fill in the numbers for our desired graph. After you fill in each number press ENTER to advance down the screen.

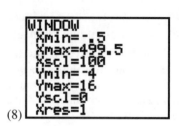

(8)

(b) Set Xmin = ⁻**0.5** (This is the lowest class boundary from the frequency table. Make sure to use the (-) key and not the − key for the negative sign.

(c) Set Xmax = 499.5 (the highest class boundary).

(d) Set Xscl = 100 (the distance between class midpoints)

(e) You must set Ymin and Ymax to cover the range of frequency values. Set Ymax = 16 (a little beyond the largest frequency of 14) and Ymin = ⁻16/4 (this is the negative of Ymax/4 and is the recommended setting for Ymin as it will leave room at the bottom of the screen for plot information.)

(f) Let Yscl = 0, so no tick marks will appear on the Y axis.

(g) Let Xres = 1 (This rule applies for all windows in this companion.)

4. Plotting the Histogram

Press TRACE. Wait for the graph to appear. Press ▶ twice for the graph in screen (9). Notice the information for each bar is displayed at the bottom of the screen as you move the cursor left and right. If you want a graph screen without this information, press GRAPH or CLEAR.

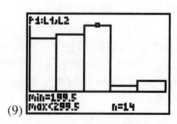

(9)

Relative Frequency Histogram

FIGURE 2-2: We continue with the relative frequency histogram for the cotinine levels of smokers. The data should still be stored in the lists as shown in screen (2). Adjust the Stat Plot1 window as shown in Screen (10). (Note we choose the relative frequencies from L3 for

(10)

Freq.) Adjust the graph window as shown in screen (11). Press TRACE to see screen (12).

Frequency Polygon

FIGURE 2-3: We construct a frequency polygon for the cotinine level data. We will fill in L5 and L6 as seen in screen (13). L5 contains the class midpoints from L1 with an extra midpoint added on each end. L6 contains the class frequencies from L2 with frequencies of 0 attributed to the two new classes.
Note: L1 and L2 could be copied to L5 and L6. (as explained on page 11) Then the two bottom values 549.5 and 0 could be added. The two top values ⁻49.5 and 0 must be inserted (as explained on page 9).

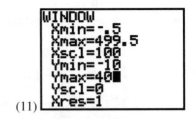
(11)

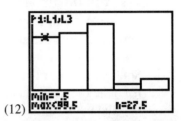
(12)

With the lists set up as in screen (13), set up Plot1 for an xyLine plot as in screen (14). Press ZOOM 9 and then TRACE in order to see the frequency polygon plot in screen (15).

Note: ZOOM 9 is called ZoomStat. It is a zoom option which uses a programmed routine to fit a graph window to the data in the Xlist and Ylist.

(13)

Ogives

FIGURE 2-4: We construct an ogive for the cotinine levels data. We begin by placing the cumulative frequencies (from L4 screen (4)) into L6 with an additional initial 0 inserted as in screen (16). L5 will contain the class boundaries which run from ⁻0.5 to 499.5. Again, set up Plot1 as in screen (14). Press ZOOM 9 and then TRACE in order to see the frequency ogive plot in screen (17). Moving the cursor, we see there are 23 cotinine level values which were less than 199.5.

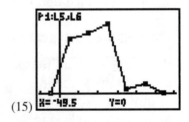
(14)

(15)

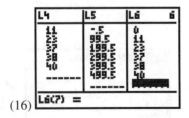
(16)

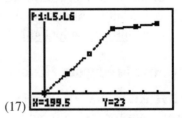
(17)

HISTOGRAMS AND FREQUENCY TABLES FROM RAW DATA

TABLE 2-1: We will obtain a histogram for the raw data set of cotinine levels for smokers.

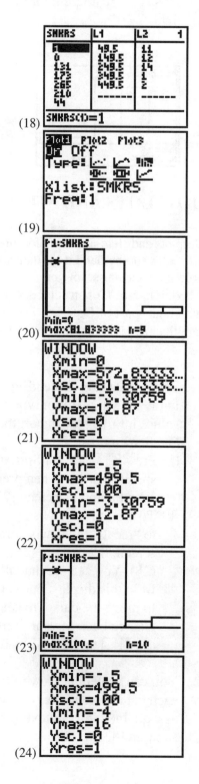

1. Enter the data into a list named SMKRS (as explained on page 10). Numbers may be entered in any order. It is often convenient to transfer large data sets from other calculators or from the Data Apps. (see Appendix, page 90). See screen (18)

    (18)

2. Set up Plot1 as in screen (19)
    (a) Choose the Xlist as SMKRS
    (b) The Freq is set at 1. This way each value in SMKRS will have frequency 1. If a data set member appears more than once in the list then its frequencies (1's) will add up to the true value of the frequency for that member.

    (19)

3. Press ZOOM 9 and then TRACE for screen (20)

    (20)

4. The results of step 3 gave us a good look at the shape of the data, but further inspection shows us that the calculator's built-in ZoomStat feature has left us with some rather odd choices for cell limits. Press WINDOW and you will see screen (21).Note the cell width or xscl = 81.833. You might wish to set your own window.

    (21)

5. Change the values in the Window to match those in screen (22). We set the Xmin at the lower class boundary, the Xmax at the upper class boundary and the Xscl at our desired cell width 100. Since this is raw data, we usually do not know enough at this point to set the parameters for the Y axis, so we will keep the ones we have for now.

    (22)

6. Press TRACE for screen (23). We cannot see the top of one of the bars, but we can use ◄ and ► to read the frequencies.

    (23)

7. Now that we know the modal class has frequency 14, we can set the window as in screen (24).

    (24)

8. Press TRACE again for the histogram in screen (25). This is the histogram for the frequency table on the right.

Class Limits Cotinine levels	L1 Midpts.	L2 Freq
0-99	49.5	11
100-199	149.5	12
200-299	249.5	14
300-399	349.5	1
400-499	449.5	2

(25)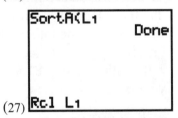

DOTPLOTS AND STEM-AND-LEAF PLOTS

Dotplots and stem-and-leaf plots are not Plot Types on the TI-83 Plus. These plots are not very difficult to do by-hand if the data set is not very large. The TI-83 Plus can aid in the process by ordering the data set for you.

FIGURE 2-5: Construct a dotplot for the movie lengths which are part of Data Set 7 in Appendix B. The movie lengths are given as integers. There are 50 values in the set.

(26)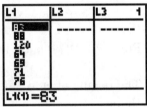

1. Sorting Data in Ascending Order.
In the Statistics Editor type the 50 movie length values into L1. (or import them from the Data Apps) See Screen (26).
(a) Press STAT 2 for SortA(. Press 2nd 1 to specify list L1 . Then press ENTER to see "Done" as in the top of Screen (27).
(b) To see the sorted list, press 2nd STO▸ 2nd 1 to "recall" the newly sorted list L1 to the main screen. See screen (27). Press ENTER for Screen (28). You can see that all of the 50 values do not fit in this display, but you can use the arrow keys to move the cursor to see them all. You could also go back to your Statistics Editor with STAT 1 to view L1 as in screen (29).

(27)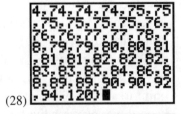

(28)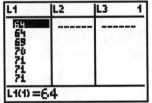

2. You can use either view to count the frequency of each data value in the set. This information is used as explained in your text to obtain a dotplot and stem-and-leaf plots.

(29)

PARETO CHARTS

Figure 2-6: The table at the right shows the results of recent research done by the FCC, categorizing the types of complaints received against U.S. phone carriers.

Complaint	Frequency
Slamming	12478
Rates	4473
Cramming	1214
Marketing	1007
Interntl. Calling	766
Access charges	614
Operators	534

1. Put the values 1, 2, 3, 4, 5, 6, 7 in L1.

2. Put the number of each of the seven types of complaints received into L2. See Screen (30).
   Note: Since a pareto chart displays data in descending order by frequency, the values in L2 must be in descending order.

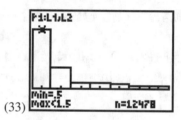
(30)

3. Set up Plot1 as a histogram as in screen (31). Set the Window as in screen (32). Press TRACE for the pareto chart displayed in screen (33).

(31)

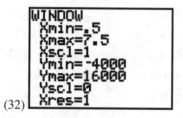
(32)

(33)

PIE CHARTS

FIGURE 2-7: Pie charts are not among the statistical plot types for the TI-83 Plus. However, the calculator can aid in the making of these plots by calculating the degree measure of the center angle for the pie wedge representing each category. We illustrate this using the data set of phone company complaints.

1. With the data on frequency of each complaint type already in L2, highlight L3, as in screen (34). Type 100L2÷sum(L2 as in the bottom of the same screen with "sum(" being pasted in by pressing 2nd STAT ▶ ▶ 5 (It is the fifth choice on the LIST<Math> menu).

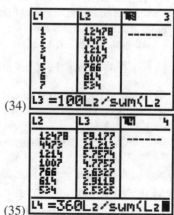
(34)

(35)

2. Press ENTER. This will give the percentage of each complaint type as seen in screen (35). Highlight L4 at the top and type 360L2/sum(L2 as in the bottom of the same screen.

3. Press ENTER. This gives the center angle (in degrees) for the pie wedge representing each accident type. See screen (36).

For example, we can see that the first row in screen (36) shows us that complaints for slamming comprised 59% of all complaints. The pie wedge for this category would have a center angle of 213°.

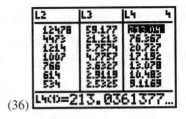

(36)

SCATTER DIAGRAMS and TIME SERIES GRAPHS

The instructions for use of the TI-83 Plus to create scatter diagrams can be found at the beginning of Chapter 9. Time series graphs are special types of scatter diagrams.

MEASURES OF CENTER

EXAMPLE Monitoring Lead in Air: Listed below are 6 measurements of the lead in the air (measured in $\mu g/m^3$) taken on 6 different days after Sept. 11, 2001 at Building 5 World Trade Center.

5.40   1.10   0.42   0.73   0.48   1.10

Mean and Median from Raw Data

1. Enter the data in L1. Press STAT ▶ 1 2nd 1 . This gives you the display in screen (37).

    Note: You have gone into the Statistics Calculations menu and chosen the first option which is 1:1-Var Stats. You have also specified that you want the statistics for the data which is stored in list L1 .

2. Press ENTER for the first output screen (38).

3. To reveal the second output screen (39), hold down the ▼ key. You will find the mean =

$$\bar{x} = \sum \frac{x}{n} = 1.538$$ on the first output screen and the

median = Med = .915 on the second output screen. Many of the other statistics displayed on the two screens will be discussed later.

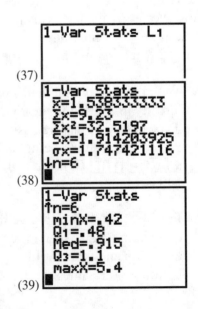

(37)

(38)

(39)

Mode

The TI-83 Plus does not automatically calculate the mode of a data set. Ordering the data and counting the frequency of each value, as discussed in the section on dotplots, will aid in finding the mode (if one exists). The modal class can be found by looking for the class with the highest frequency in a frequency table. (See page 17 of this chapter.)

Midrange

EXAMPLE Monitoring Lead in Air: Find the midrange of the six data values

$$5.40 \quad 1.10 \quad 0.42 \quad 0.73 \quad 0.48 \quad 1.10$$

Two of the values on the second output screen are **Min** and **Max**. These are the lowest and highest values in the data set. We can use

the output on screen (39) to calculate midrange $= \dfrac{\text{Max} + \text{Min}}{2} = \dfrac{5.4 + 0.42}{2} = 2.910$.

EXAMPLE Cotinine Levels of Smokers : We previously created list SMKRS or brought it in from the Data Apps. We will now find the mean, median and midrange for this data set.

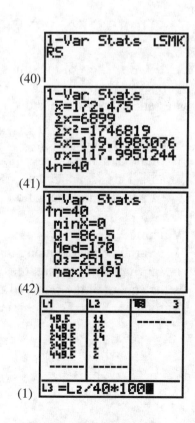

1. Press [STAT] [▶] [1] to get the display "1-Var Stats" on your main screen as in screen (40). You must then choose your list SMKRS from the Lists menu. Do this by pressing [2nd] [STAT] to pull up the Lists menu and then look down the menu for SMKRS. Take the cursor down to highlight the number by the list then [ENTER]. At this point you should see screen (40).

(40)

(41)

2. Press [ENTER] for screen (41) and move the cursor down for screen (42). We see the mean cotinine level is 172.5. The median is 170. The midrange is $\dfrac{\text{Max} + \text{Min}}{2} = \dfrac{491 + 0}{2} = 245.5$.

(42)

Mean from a Frequency Distribution

TABLE 2-9: The frequency table of the cotinine levels of smokers is repeated from page 13. Class midpoints will be stored in L1 and frequencies in L2 as was done earlier in Screen (1).

(1)

1. Press STAT ▶ 1 2nd 1 , 2nd 2 to get screen (43).

   Note: You have asked for the 1 Var Stats as before, but this time you specified two lists separated by a comma. The TI-83 Plus is programmed to treat the second list as frequencies. The , key is located above the 7.

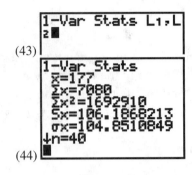

2. Press ENTER for screen (44). We see that the mean value calculated from the frequency table is 177.0 which is slightly larger than the true mean of the data, 172.5.

Weighted Mean

EXAMPLE: Find the mean of three tests scores (85, 90, 75) if the first tests counts 20%, the second counts 30%, and the third test counts for 50% of the final grade.

Put the scores in L1 and the weights in L2, as in screen (45). Press STAT ▶ 1 2nd 1 , 2nd 2 as in screen (43). Press ENTER for screen (46). We see that the weighted mean is $\bar{x} = 81.5$.

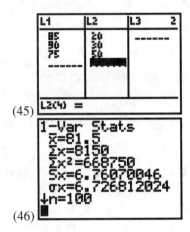

MEASURES OF VARIATION

EXAMPLE : The waiting times (in minutes) of three Mulberry Bank customers are 1, 3, and 14. Find the range, standard deviation and variance of this data.

1. **Standard Deviation**

   With the data in L1, press STAT ▶ 1 2nd 1 ENTER. This sequence gives screens (47), (48) and (49). The standard deviation is Sx = 7 minutes.

2. **Variance**

   The variance is not among the statistics given by the 1-Var Stats display, but it is easy to calculate since it is the square of the standard deviation. In this case, Variance = $Sx^2 = 7^2 = 49$ min^2.

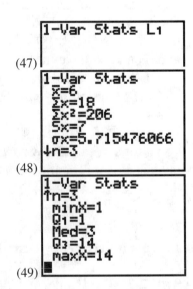

3. **Range**

The range is given by maxX - minX = 14 − 1 = 13 minutes.

4. **Vars 5: Statistics Menu for Pasting in Sx**

(a) Press $\boxed{\text{VARS}}$ for the VARS menu screen (50)

(b) Press $\boxed{5}$ for the Statistics sub menu screen (51)

(c) Press $\boxed{3}$ and Sx is pasted onto your main screen.

(d) Press $\boxed{\text{ENTER}}$ to see that Sx is 7 as in the top of screen (52)

(e) Press $\boxed{x^2}$ and then $\boxed{\text{ENTER}}$ to again see variance = 49.

Note: This option would save the effort of typing in all the digits of Sx (not a difficult task in this example). It is important to know that you can only paste Sx (or any other statistic) after you have performed 1-Var Stats on your current data set, otherwise the statistics stored will be from some past calculation.

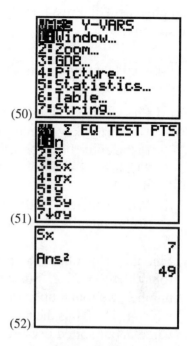

(50)
(51)
(52)

Standard Deviation from a Frequency Distribution

EXAMPLE: Cotinine Levels of Smokers: Find the standard deviation of the 40 cotinine level values summarized in the Table at the beginning of this chapter.

This is done using the same procedure used to find the *mean* from a frequency table. In fact, if we look at the output on screen (44), we see that Sx = 106.1868213. We can look at the output from screen (41) to see the standard deviation calculated using all the data values is Sx = 119.4983076.

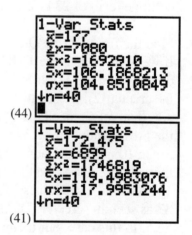

(44)
(41)

MEASURES OF RELATIVE STANDING

Quartiles and Percentiles

EXAMPLE Cotinine Levels of Smokers: We again examine the data set which was earlier stored in a list called SMKRS.

To begin, we must have the data sorted in ascending order. Press $\boxed{\text{STAT}}$ $\boxed{2}$ for SortA. Press $\boxed{\text{2nd}}$ $\boxed{\text{STAT}}$ to get the menu of all lists. Look down it for SMKRS. Cursor down until the number next to SMKRS is highlighted

then press ENTER Press ENTER again, and you should
see screen (53).

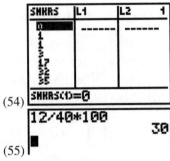

(53)

1. Find the percentile corresponding to the
    cotinine level of 112.

    (a) Press STAT 1 then highlight on SMKRS and
        Use the ▾ key to move down list SMKRS
        to the entry 112. See screen (54). We note that
        112 is the 13th entry, so there are 12 values less
        than 112.

    (54)

    (b) We calculate (12/40)*100 = 30. Thus 112 is the
        30th percentile. See screen (55)

    (55)

2. Find the value of the 68th percentile or P$_{68}$.
    (68/100)*40 = 27.2. Since this is not a whole
    number, we round up to the nearest whole number
    which is 28. Thus the 68th percentile is the 28th
    value in our sorted list. We find this value to be a
    cotinine level of 234, screen (56).

    (56)

3. Find the first quartile Q$_1$.
    If we look back at the TI-83 Plus' Q$_1$ statistic
    displayed in the 1-Var Stats calculations for SMKRS
    in screen (42), we see that the value is Q1=86.5.
    Alternatively, since Q$_1$ = P$_{25}$, we could proceed as in
    the previous example. We find (25/100)*40 = 10.
    Since 10 is a whole number, our algorithm would
    then require us to find the value midway between the
    10th and 11th data values. These values are 86 and
    87 as seen in screen (57). Thus Q1 = (86+87)/2 =
    86.5. In this case, our method has yielded the same
    result as that of the TI-83 Plus.

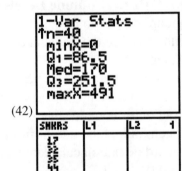

(42)

(57)

BOXPLOTS AND FIVE-NUMBER SUMMARY

EXAMPLE Cotinine Levels of Smokers
Use the data set containing 40 values of cotinine levels
of smokers to
(a)   Find the values of the five-number summary.
(b)   Construct a boxplot.

(a) We have seen the five-number summary for this data set already. It is on the second screen of output for the 1-Var Stats for our SMKRS list. This was screen (42). The five-number summary is minX=0, Q1=86,5, Med=170, Q3=251.5, and maxX=491.

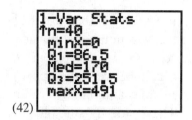

(42)

(b) **Boxplot (or Box and Whisker Diagram)**

1. Press [2nd] [Y=] to get the Stat Plots menu and then [1] to get the set-up for Stat Plot1. Set up Stat Plot1 as in screen (58). We choose the fifth plot type. This is the *skeletal* boxplot which is described in your text. **Note:** The fourth plot type is a *modified* boxplot which is a slightly more complex variation on the skeletal boxplot presented in the text.

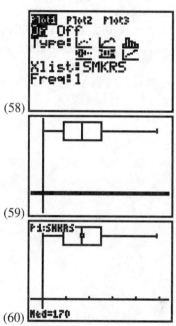

(58)

(59)

(60)

2. Press [ZOOM] [9] for the boxplot of Screen (59)

3. Press [TRACE] then use the [◄] and [►] keys to display the **five-number summary**. This gives a display like screen (60).

Comparing Data Sets with Side-by-Side Boxplots

EXAMPLE Cholesterol Levels of Men and Women: We compare the cholesterol levels of 40 females and 40 males as seen in Data Set 1 in Appendix B. We have stored the females' cholesterol levels in L1 and the males' cholesterol levels in L2.

1. Press [2nd] [Y=] to get the Stat Plots menu and then [1] to get the set-up for Stat Plot1. Set up Stat Plot1 as in screen (61).

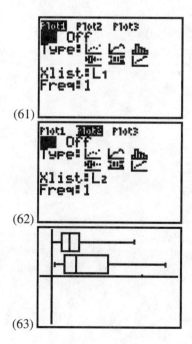

(61)

(62)

(63)

2. Press [2nd] [Y=] to get the Stat Plots menu and then [2] to get the set-up for Stat Plot2. Set up Stat Plot2 as in screen (62).

3. Press [ZOOM] [9] to see the two boxplots of screen (63).

4. Press ⟨TRACE⟩ then use the ◄ and ► keys to display
    the five-number summary. This gives a display like
    screen (64). You can use the ▲ and ▼ keys to
    toggle between the upper plot which is that of the
    females and the lower plot which is for the males.
    These side-by-side plots clearly indicate that males,
    in general, have higher cholesterol levels than
    females and that the cholesterol levels of males tend
    to be more variable than those of females.

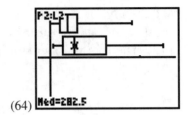

(64)

Note: Since the TI-83 Plus has three StatPlots, it can be used to
    plot box and whisker plots for three different data sets on the
    same graph.

3   Probability

In this chapter you will learn how your TI-83 Plus calculator can be used in the calculation of probabilities. There are several built-in functions which make this work much simpler, including the *change to fraction function,* the *raise to power key,* and the *Math Probability menu* which includes options to make the calculation of factorials, combinations and permutations very easy. You will also be introduced to the concept of simulation. This process can be used to approximate probabilities. Your exposure to the process may have the added benefit of giving you a deeper understanding of the concepts of probability.

TWO USEFUL FUNCTIONS

Change to Fraction Function

EXAMPLE Birth Genders: In reality, more boys are born than girls. In one typical group, there are 205 newborn babies, 105 of whom are boys. If one baby is randomly selected from the group, what is the probability that the baby is not a boy?

4. Using the Law of Complements, we decide the answer is 100/205=0.488. See the first line of screen (1).

5. Press [MATH] [1] (This chooses the *change to fraction function.*)

6. Press [ENTER]. You should see Screen (1). The result

    is the probability written as a reduced fraction $\frac{20}{41}$.

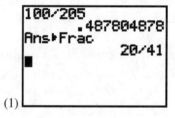

(1)

Note: This function is handy when you wish to give your probability answer as a fraction.

The Raise-to-the-Power Key
The Probability of "at Least One"

EXAMPLE Gender of Children: Find the probability of a couple having at least one girl among three children.

1.   Find the probability of the complement.
     P(boy and boy and boy) = 0.5*0.5*0.5 = 0.5^3.
     Type 0.5 ⃞^ ⃞3. Then press ⃞ENTER for 0.125. You
     will see the first two lines of screen (2).

Note: Keep in mind the answer you have now is the complement of
the answer you seek.

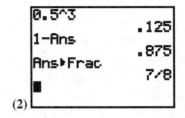

2.   Press ⃞1 ⃞− ⃞2nd ⃞(-). This takes your answer from
     above and subtracts it from 1 as seen in screen (2).
     Press ⃞ENTER for 0.875. This could be changed to the
     fraction 7/8 as shown in the bottom of screen (2).

(2)

PROBABILITIES THROUGH SIMULATION

Finding probabilities of events can sometimes be difficult. We can often gain knowledge
and insight into the problem by developing a simulation of it. The techniques used in the
examples in this section build upon one another. Thus each example assumes you are
familiar with the ones preceding it.

EXAMPLE Gender Selection: When testing techniques of gender selection, medical
researchers need to know probability values of different outcomes, such as the probability
of getting at least 60 girls among 100 children. Assuming that male and female births are
equally likely, describe a simulation that results in the gender of 100 newborn babies.

We will perform this simulation by generating 100
random 0's and 1's. Each will be equally likely.

1.   We begin by setting the "seed" for our random
     number generator as 136. (The reason for this step is
     to set your calculator, so it will generate the same
     random numbers as generated by the calculator used
     in this manual. This step is not necessary when
     performing your own simulations.) Press 136 ⃞STO▸
     ⃞MATH ⃞◂ ⃞1 ⃞ENTER for the top of screen (3).

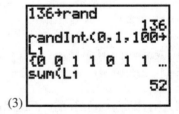

2.   Type ⃞MATH ⃞◂ ⃞5 to get the "randInt" prompt on the
     main screen. Then type 0,1,100 ⃞STO▸ ⃞2nd ⃞1 ⃞ENTER
     to have the TI-83 Plus generate one hundred 0's and
     1's and store them in L1. See middle of screen (3).
     We can see the results which begin with {0 0 1 1 0 1
     1, …} These can be translated as {B B G G B G
     G…}if we let the 1's represent girls and the 0's
     represent boys.

(3)

3. We can sum the elements in list L1 to find out how many 1's (girls) we had in this simulation of 100 births. Press [2nd] [STAT] [▶] [▶] [5] [2nd] [1] [ENTER] to sum the elements of L1. We see that this time we had 52 girls. See screen (3).

Note: We did not have 60 or more girls in this simulation. In order to get an idea of the probability of at least 60 girls in 100 births, you would have to perform the simulation repeatedly, keeping track of how often the event of 60 or more girls occurred.

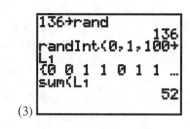
(3)

EXAMPLE Same Birthday: One classic exercise in probability is the *birthday problem* in which we find the probability that in a class of 25 students at least 2 students have the same birthday. Ignoring leap years, describe a simulation of the experiment that yields birthdays of 25 students in a class.

We will perform this simulation by generating 25 random integers between 1 and 365 (representing the 365 possible birthdays in a non-leap year.)

1. Again we set the seed so as to obtain the same outputs as this manual. Press 123 [STO▶] [MATH] [◀] [1] [ENTER] for the top of screen (4).

2. Next generate 25 random integers between 1 and 365, store them in L1and sort L1. Do this by typing [MATH] [◀] [5] to get the "randInt" prompt then typing 1, 365, 25 [STO▶] [2nd] [1] [ALPHA] [.] [STAT] [2] [2nd] [1] [ENTER] to see the "Done" as in screen (4). Note the [ALPHA] [.] sequence yielded a colon on the screen. The colon can be used to tie several statements together in one line.

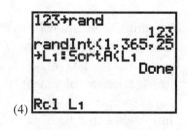
(4)

3. We wish to see the results of our simulation, so recall L1 to the screen with [2nd] [STO▶] [2nd] [1] for the bottom of screen (4) and then press [ENTER] for screen (5). We can see that two students in this simulated class had the same birthday on the 190th day of the year.

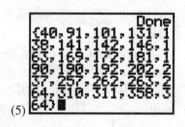
(5)

4. To repeat this simulation without retyping all the commands, simply press [2nd] [ENTER] [ENTER]. This sequence yields the "ENTRY" command which repeats the last command line. Now press [2nd] [STO▶] [2nd] [1] to

recall list L1 as in screen (6). Press ENTER to check the
next set of results. This set is shown in screen (7). It
shows no birthday matches in this simulated group of 25
students.

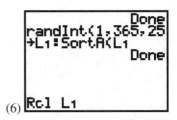

(6)

Thus far we have seen a 50% chance of a birthday match
in a group of 25. Naturally, the simulation should be
repeated many more times to get a better estimate of the
actual probability of this event.

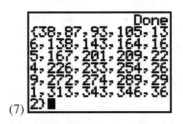

(7)

EXAMPLE Simulating Dice: Describe a procedure for
simulating the rolling of a pair of six-sided dice.

1. This time we seed the random number generator
    with 4321. (Again, this step is only necessary if you
    are trying to duplicate the results presented in this
    guide.)

2. To generate two random integers between 1 and 6
    type MATH ◄ 5 to get the "randInt" prompt then
    type 1, 6,2. Press ENTER. If you used the seed from
    step 1, you should see the result (4,3) as in screen
    (8). Continue to press ENTER to generate new rolls as
    shown in the bottom of screen (8).

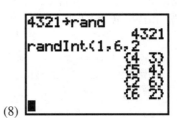

(8)

3. To quickly generate 100 sets of two rolls and
    calculate their sums, you could proceed as follows.
    (a) Generate 100 integers between 1 and 6 and store
    in L1. (See top of screen (9)).
    (b) Generate 100 integers between 1 and 6 and store
    in L2. (See middle of screen (9)).
    (c) Add L1 and L2 and store the results in L3. (See
    bottom of screen (9)).
    (d) Press STAT 1 to see the results in your lists as
    in screen (10).
    (e) Screen (11) shows a histogram of the results of
    this simulation. This histogram is for the data set
    consisting of the sums of the two rolls. This set was
    stored in L3. The Window settings were Xmin = 1.5,
    Xmax = 12.5, Xscl = 1, Ymin = -8, Ymax = 25. This
    simulation could be used to approximate the
    probability of rolling a certain sum. For example, we
    can see that our 100 rolls yielded 21 sums of 7. Thus
    we could estimate the probability of rolling a 7 to be

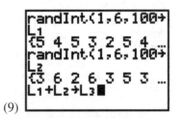

(9)

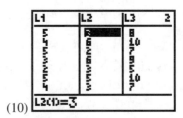

(10)

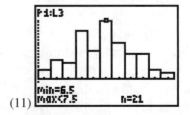

(11)

21%. (In actuality the value is 1/6 or 16.7%. More simulations would no doubt lead us closer to the truth.)

COUNTING

Factorials

Notation: The factorial symbol is !

EXAMPLE Routes to All 50 Capitals: How many different routes are possible if you must visit each of the 50 state capitals?

By applying the factorial rule, we know that the 50 state capitals can be arranged in a total of 50! Ways. We must calculate 50!. Do so by first typing 50. Then press MATH ◄ 4 to locate the factorial (!) symbol on the Math Probability submenu. Press ENTER to see the results of the calculation of this very large product. In screen (12) we see the result is approximately 3E64 or $3*10^{64}$ or 3 followed by 64 zeros – in any case a lot of possible routes!

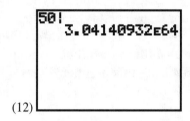

(12)

Permutations

EXAMPLE Television Programming: You have just been hired to determine the programming for the Fox television network. When selecting the shows to be shown on Monday night, you find that you have 27 shows available and you must select 4 of them. Because of lead-in effects, the order of the shows is important. How many different sequences of 4 shows are possible when there are 27 shows available?

We know that we need to calculate the number of permutations of 4 objects selected from 27 available objects. Begin by typing 27. Press MATH ◄ 2 to select nPr from the Math Probability summenu. Then type 4. Press ENTER to see the result 421,200 as in screen (13).

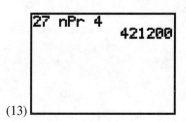

(13)

Combinations

EXAMPLE Maine Lottery: In the Maine lottery, a player wins or shares in the jackpot by selecting the correct 6-number combination when 6 different numbers from 1 through 42 are drawn. If a player selects one particular 6-number combination, find the probability of winning the jackpot. (Order is irrelevant).

Because 6 different numbers are selected from 42 and order is irrelevant, we know we must calculate the number of combinations of 6 objects chosen from 42. This will tells us the total number of possible lottery outcomes. We begin by typing 42. Then press [MATH] [◂] [3] to select the option nCr from the Math Probability submenu. Then type 6. Press [ENTER] to see that there are 5,245,786 possible combinations of 6 numbers. The probability of a single combination winning is found by inverting this number (Press [x⁻¹] [ENTER]). See screen (14).

(14)
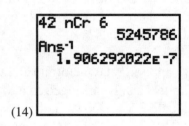

4   Probability Distributions

In this chapter you will learn how your TI-83 Plus calculator can be used when working with probability distribution functions. First, you will learn how to use the calculator when given a probability function in the form of a table of values for the random variable with associated probabilities. You will also learn how to calculate probabilities of random variables which have the binomial or poisson distribution. In both cases, you will be shown how to calculate on the Home screen using the formulas for these distributions and alternatively how to use built-in distribution functions in the DISTR menu. Either alternative alleviates the need to use probability tables and, in fact, yields answers with more accuracy than the tables.

PROBABILITY DISTRIBUTIONS BY TABLES

EXAMPLE Gender of Children: Table 4-1, reproduced below, describes the probability distribution for the number of girls among 14 randomly selected newborn babies.

X	0	1	2	3	4	5	6	7	8	9	10	11	12	13	14
P(x)	0.0+	0.001	0.006	0.022	0.061	0.122	0.183	0.209	0.183	0.122	0.061	0.022	0.006	0.002	0.0+

Probability Histogram

To plot the probability histogram from the table follow these steps:

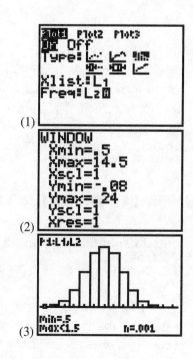

1. Put the x values in L1 and the P(x) values in L2. (Type 0, not 0+ for the first and last values.)
Note: Sum(L2) = 0.999 which is approximately 1 as expected.

(1)

2. Set up Plot1 and the WINDOW as in screens (1) and (2). Press [TRACE] for the probability histogram in screen (3). The selection of WINDOW values for this histogram was made similarly to examples shown in Chapter 2.

(2)

Mean, Variance and Standard Deviation

EXAMPLE Gender of Children: Use the probability distribution to find the mean number of girls (among 14), the variance, and the standard deviation.

(3)

1. As before, put the x values in L1 and the P(x) values in L2.

2. Press STAT ▶ 1 2nd 1 , 2nd 2 for screen (4) and then press ENTER for screen (5). The value of the mean μ is given on this screen as $\bar{x} = 7$. The standard deviation σ is given by σx = 1.876038251, so the variance is $\sigma^2 = (1.87604)^2 = 3.5195$.

Note: We have n = .999 ≈ 1 for the sum of the probabilities. If n were exactly 1, then this result would agree exactly with the following one.

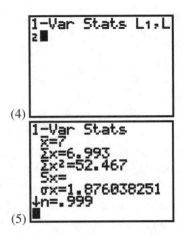

(4)

(5)

Expected Value/Mean by the Formula $\sum [x * P(x)]$

EXAMPLE Gender of Children: Use the probability distribution to find the expected number of girls or the mean number of girls (among 14 births).

1. Again put the x values in L1 and the P(x) values in L2. This is partially shown in screen (6).

2. With L3 highlighted at the top, multiply L1 by L2 as shown in the bottom line of screen (6). Press ENTER for screen (7).

3. Press 2nd MODE to Quit and return to the home screen. Then press 2nd STAT ▶ ▶ 5 to paste the sum function from the LIST <Math> submenu on the home screen. Then press 2nd 3 for L3 as seen in screen (8). Press ENTER to find the sum of the entries in L3 which turns out to be 6.993 ≈ 7.

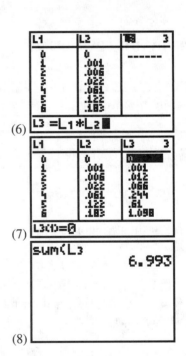

(6)

(7)

(8)

BINOMIAL DISTRIBUTION

Binomial Probability Formula

$$P(x) = nCx * p^x (1-p)^{n=x} \quad \text{for } x = 0, 1, 2, ..., n$$

EXAMPLE Analysis of Multiple Choice Answers:
Find the probability of getting exactly 3 correct answers when random guesses are made for 4 multiple choice

questions each having five answer choices . That is, find P(3) given that n = 4, x = 3, p = 0.2, and q = 0.8.

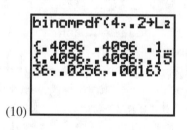

(9)

Type on the home screen to emulate what you see in screen (9). You can find the nCr function in the MATH <PRB> submenu (at [MATH] [◄] [3]). Press [ENTER] to calculate the probability as 0.0256.

Built-in Binomial pdf and cdf Calculators

EXAMPLE Analysis of Multiple Choice Answers:
We will extend the above example and show how the TI-83 Plus' built-in functions for the binomial distribution can be used for a variety of problem types.

(a) Find the complete probability distribution.
To get the complete table of values and store it in L2 , press [2nd] [VARS] [0] to choose the binompdf from the DISTR menu. Then type 4 [,] 0.2 to specify that n = 4 and p = 0.2. Next press [STO►] [2nd] [2] to store results in L2 then [ENTER] for the top of screen (10). Next press [2nd] [STO►] [2nd] [2] [ENTER] to recall L2 to the screen, so you can read the entries as in the bottom of screen (10).

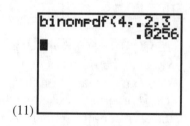

(10)

(b) Find the probability of getting *exactly* 3 answers correct.
To find the probability at a single point, we use the "binompdf" function. Press [2nd] [VARS] [0] 4 [,] .2 [,] 3 and then [ENTER] for the answer .0256 as seen in screen (11). Of course, the answer agrees with what is seen in screen (10) above.
Note: pdf stands for probability density function

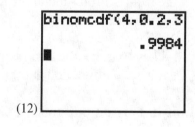

(11)

(c) Find the probability of *at most* 3 answers correct.
At most means "less than or equal to", so the probability of at most 3 is in fact P(0)+P(1)+P(2)+P(3). This can be found by using the built-in "binomcdf" function. This is the A: option in the DISTR menu. Type [2nd] [VARS] [ALPHA] [MATH] to paste "binomcdf(" on your home screen. Then type 4,0.2,3 and press [ENTER] for screen (12). The answer is .9984.

(12)

(d) Find the probability of *at least* 3 correct answers. *At least* means "greater than or equal to". Thus we seek

P(3)+P(4) which is the same as 1 - [P(0)+P(1)+P(2)].
Screen (13) shows two possible ways to find this answer
which is .0272.

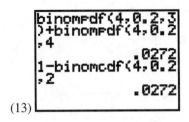

(13)

POISSON DISTRIBUTION

EXAMPLE World War II Bombs: (The problem below has been extended to answer
more questions in order to better show off the capabilities of the TI-83 Plus). In analyzing
hits by V-1 buzz bombs in World War II, South London was subdivided into 576 regions,
each with an area of 0.25 sq. km. A total of 535 bombs hit the combined area of 576
regions for an average of 535/576 = 0.929 hits per region. If a region is randomly selected,
use the Poisson distribution to answer the following questions.

Poisson Probability Formula $P(x) = \mu^x e^{-\mu}/x!$

(a) Find the probability that the region was hit *exactly*
twice.
Recalling that in this problem $\mu = 0.929$, and noting that
for this question x = 2, we evaluate the above formula
on the home screen as seen in screen (14). Here is the
key sequence, which we will break down and explain
below: 2 [STO▸] [X,T,Θ,n] [ALPHA] [.] 0.929[^] [X,T,Θ,n] [×]
[2nd] [LN] [(-)] 0.929 [)] [÷] [X,T,Θ,n] [MATH] [◄] [4] [ENTER].

(14)

- The 2 [STO▸] [X,T,Θ,n] [ALPHA] [.] stores 2 as the x-
  value and adds a colon, so the function evaluation
  step can be placed on the same line.
- The [2nd] [LN] keystrokes get the exponential function for
  the $e^{-\mu}$ part of the formula.
- The [MATH] [◄] [4] gets the factorial "!"symbol from
  the Math <Prob> menu for the x! part of the
  formula.
- Note that we could now press [2nd] [ENTER] and use the
  [▲] key to move the cursor up and change x to
  evaluate the function at other values.

Built-in Poisson pdf and cdf Calculators

(a) Find the probability that the region was hit *exactly*
twice.
We can use the built-in function "poissonpdf" to find the
probability of a Poisson variable being equal to some

given value x. This function is located in the DISTR menu at option B (2nd VARS ALPHA APPS). Paste on the function and fill in the rest as in screen (15). Press ENTER to see the same result as before. Note that the poissonpdf function requires two inputs: μ and x.

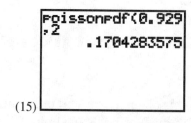

(15)

(b) Find the probability that the region was hit *at most* twice. The built in function "poissoncdf" can be used to find cumulative probabilities of a Poisson variable up to and including a given value x. This function is the C option in the DIST menu. 2nd VARS ALPHA PRGM). Paste it on the main screen and fill in the rest as in screen (16). We see the cumulative probability is .9323. Note the inputs for the poissoncdf function were the same as for the pdf function, μ and x.

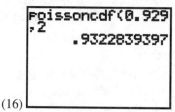

(16)

(c) Find the probability that the region was hit *at least* twice.
We need the probability of greater than or equal to 2 hits. This is P(2)+P(3)+P(4)+... = 1 – [P(0)+P(1)].
We see that we need 1 – poissoncdf(0.929,1). We type this on the home screen and ENTER for the answer .2381 as seen on screen (17). Remember from above, poissoncdf is found at 2nd VARS ALPHA PRGM.

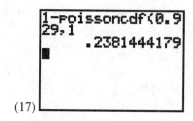

(17)

(d) Find the probability that the region was hit between 2 and 6 times.
We see that we need P(2)+P(3)+P(4)+P(5)+P(6). We note that this will require us to find the value of poissoncdf(0.929,6) – poissoncdf(0.929,1). We do so on screen (18). It is 0.23809.

Note: It is important to remember to close the parentheses after "poissoncdf(0.929,6)". Otherwise your TI-83 Plus will not know that you are done with that poissoncdf and ready to move to another one.

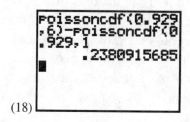

(18)

5   Normal Probability Distribution

In this chapter you will use your TI-83 Plus to aid you in several types of problems dealing with the Normal Probability Distribution. First, you will learn to use the built-in function *normalcdf* to obtain probabilities associated with normal random variables. You will also learn to use the built-in function *invnorm* to obtain percentiles from a given normal distribution (that is, when given a probability value you will find the associated value of the normal variable). Both of these functions are on the DISTR menu at 2nd VARS. Using them will alleviate the need to use the tables in the text. You will learn to do a simulation which illustrates the Central Limit Theorem and to approximate a binomial distribution with a normal distribution. You will learn how to obtain a *normal quantile plot*. This plot, described in the text, is used to determine if a given set of data might come from a population with a normal distribution. Finally, you will be introduced to a built-in feature which can generate random normal data for you to use in simulations of your own.

FINDING PROBABILITIES FOR A NORMAL RANDOM VARIABLE

We will use the built-in function "normalcdf." This function is in the DISTR menu as option 2. 2nd VARS 2). It requires 4 inputs. They are (a,b,μ,σ). Here the "a" and "b" denote two values between which you want the probability. As you might guess, μ and σ represent the mean and standard deviation of the normal variable. (If we do not put in values for μ and σ, the calculator assumes the distribution is *standard* normal and thus μ = 0 and σ = 1). We will use the function on several examples to follow.

Standard Normal Probabilities

EXAMPLE Scientific Thermometer: This example is *standard normal*.
(a) Find the probability of a reading *less than* 1.58. Press 2nd VARS 2 to paste up the "normalcdf(". Then type –E99,1.58,0,1 and ENTER. To get the "E" press 2nd . See screen (1).

Note: The value –E99 is a number which is VERY much less than 1.58. We used it in the "a" position because we had no value at which to start our probability area, and we wished to get as much of the area below 1.58 as possible. Note also as shown in the lower part of Screen (1) that we did not have to specify the mean and standard deviation for a *standard* normal probability problem

(1)

```
normalcdf( -E99,1
.58,0,1
          .942946563
normalcdf( -E99,1
.58
          .942946563
■
```

(b) Find the probability of a reading *above* –1.23.
We proceed similarly to problem (a) but with different
values for "a" and "b." We get 0.8906. See Screen (2).
Note: This time we used E99 in the "b" position because it was a
"greater than" problem and we had no value for the end of our
probability area.

(c) Find the probability of a reading *between* –2 and 1.5.
This is very straight-forward because in *between*
problems, we are given values for inputs "a" and "b."
See Screen (3).

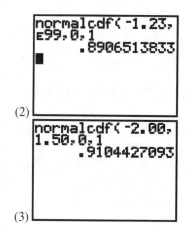

(2)

(3)

Non-Standard Normal Probabilities

There is really no difference in the TI-83 Plus' procedure for standard and non-standard
normal probabilities except for the fact that in the non-standard normal problems the mean
and standard deviation are required inputs for the normalcdf function.

EXAMPLE Designing Cars: The sitting heights of drivers must be considered in the
design of a new car model. Men have sitting heights that are normally distributed with a
mean of 36.0 in. and a standard deviation of 1.4 in. If a man is randomly selected, find
the probability that he has a sitting height less than 38.8 in.

We know that we need to see normalcdf(¯E99,38.8,36.0,1.4) on our home screen. Type
this in and press ENTER. We get 0.9772 (See the top of screen (4)).

An alternative is to have the calculator draw a shaded
graph of the area in addition to calculating it. This is a
two step procedure, but <u>first</u> turn off all StatPlots.
1. **Setting the WINDOW**. See screen (5).
   We have used the following criteria to set our
   window values: Xmin = $\mu - 3\sigma$ = 36-3(1.4)=31.8
   Xmax = $\mu + 3\sigma$ = 36+3(1.4) = 40.2
   Xscl and Yscl = 0
   Ymin = -.1/ σ = -.1/1.4 = -.0714
   Ymax = 0.4/ σ = 0.4/1.4 = .2857

2. **Getting the Graph:** Press 2nd VARS ▶ 1 to get
   the "ShadeNorm(" pasted on your screen as in
   bottom screen (4). Fill in the values of a, b, μ and σ
   as usual. Press ENTER for the shaded graph in screen
   (6). We can see the Area =.97725. This area is
   equivalent to the probability we were seeking.

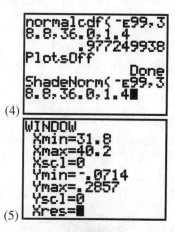

(4)

(5)

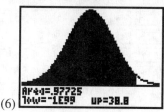

(6)

FINDING VALUES OF A NORMAL RANDOM VARIABLE (INVERSE NORMAL PROBLEMS)

The InvNorm Function

EXAMPLE Hip Breadth and Airplane Seats: In designing seats to be installed in commercial aircraft, engineers want to make the seats wide enough to fit 98% of all males. Men have hip breadths that are normally distributed with a mean of 14.4 in. and a standard deviation of 1.0 inches. Find P_{98}. That is, find the hip breadth of men that separates the bottom 98% from the top 2%.

Press [2nd] [VARS] [3] to paste the "invnorm(" onto your home screen. This function needs three inputs: p, μ, and σ. Here p represents the percentile we desire to know. So for this problem we input 0.98,14.4,1 and [ENTER]. We see that a hip breadth of 16.4557 inches separates the bottom 98% from the top 2%. See screen (7).

Note: Make sure to use the decimal value of the desired percentile (for example 0.98 and not 98).

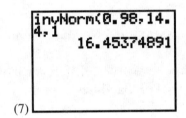

(7)

CENTRAL LIMIT THEOREM

As the sample size increases the sampling distribution of the sample means approaches a normal distribution.

We perform a simulation of the example in the text which looked at the last 4 digits of 50 randomly selected social security numbers. In this simulation, you will generate 50 sets of 4 digit numbers on the TI-83 Plus and look at the distribution of the numbers selected and the distribution of their means.

1. Set the seed, so your random number generator will duplicate the results shown here. Press 4321 [STO▸] [MATH] [◄] [1] [ENTER]. See top of Screen (8)

2. Set up 4 lists of 50 random integers between 0 and 9. This is partially shown in screen (8). The keystrokes are as follows:

    [MATH] [◄] [5] 0 [,] 9 [,] 50 [STO▸] [2nd] [1] [ENTER]
    [MATH] [◄] [5] 0 [,] 9 [,] 50 [STO▸] [2nd] [2] [ENTER]
    [MATH] [◄] [5] 0 [,] 9 [,] 50 [STO▸] [2nd] [3] [ENTER]
    [MATH] [◄] [5] 0 [,] 9 [,] 50 [STO▸] [2nd] [4] [ENTER]

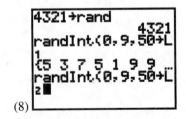

(8)

Note: Remember you can use [2nd] [ENTER] to recall the last entry and make this sequence of steps easier. See page 6.

3. Find the mean of each of the 50 rows using the following (see last line of screen (9)):
(L1+L2+L3+L4)/4 [STO▸] L5 [ENTER].

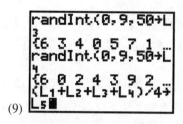

(9)

4. Press [STAT] [1] to view your lists as in screens (10) and (11). Note the means in L5 are tending toward the middle of the distribution.

5. Set StatPlot 1 to get a histogram of the data in L1. Set up the WINDOW as in screens (12). Press [TRACE] for screen (13). Note that the data in L1 are fairly uniformly distributed between 0 and 9. The other lists would behave similarly.

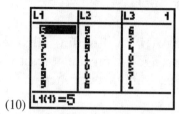

(10)

6. Now change the setup of StatPlot1 to graph the means stored in L5. Press [TRACE] for screen (14). Note that this histogram is much more *normally* distributed than that of screen (13). This is as predicted by the Central Limit Theorem.

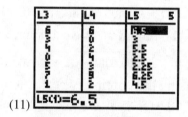

(11)

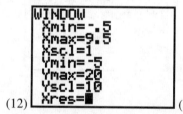

(12)

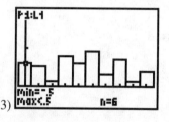

(13)

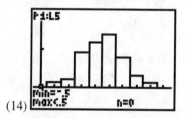

(14)

EXAMPLE Ski Gondola Safety: Given that the population of men have weights that are normally distributed with a mean of 172 lb and a standard deviation of 29 lb,

(a) Find the probability that if an individual man is randomly selected, his weight will be greater than 167 pounds.

The probability is 0.5084. See top of screen (15).
(b) Find the probability that 12 randomly selected men will have a mean weight that is greater than 167 pounds.

(15)

The probability is 0.7248. See bottom of screen (15) and note that the only thing that has changed is the standard error which is now $29/\sqrt{12}$.

Note: In the above, our answers differ slightly from those in the text because we did not use the tables. The TI-83 Plus solutions are actually more precise because they did not suffer from round-off error.

NORMAL DISTRIBUTION AS AN APPROXIMATION TO THE BINOMIAL DISTRIBUTION

If np $\geq$ 5 and n(1-p) $\geq$ 5, then the binomial random variable is approximately normally distributed with the mean and standard deviation given by μ = np and $\sigma = \sqrt{np(1-p)}$

EXAMPLE Loading Airliners: Find the probability that among 200 randomly selected passengers there are at least 120 men. Assume that the population of passengers consists of an equal number of men and women.

First, we check to see if we can use the normal approximation. We see that np = 200(0.50) = 100 > 5 and that n(1-p) = 200(0.50) = 100 > 5. So we can use the normal approximation to the binomial. We can approximate μ = np and $\sigma = \sqrt{np(1-p)}$ by μ = 100 and

$\sigma = \sqrt{200(0.5)(1-0.5)} = 7.07$

Using the continuity correction to find P(X>120), we need to start at 119.5 and continue on to the right. See screen (16). We obtain a probability of 0.0029.
At the bottom of screen (16), we check the answer by using the binomcdf function discussed in Ch. 4. We find the actual probability is 0.00284. We see that the approximation of .0029 was quite accurate.

(16)

NORMAL QUANTILE PLOTS

EXAMPLE Boston Rainfall: In Data Set 11 of Appendix B, use the 52 rainfall amounts listed for Sundays in Boston and test for normality.

1. Get the data set into L1. You can type it, transfer it from another calculator, or transfer it from Data Apps (see Appendix, page 90).

(17)

2. Set up StatPlot1 as seen in screen (17). Note that the normal quantile plot is the <u>last</u> type. Make sure you choose X as the data axis.

3. Press ZOOM 9 for screen (18). Note the normal quantile plot is nowhere near linear and thus the rainfall data is not at all normally distributed.

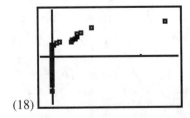

(18)

GENERATING RANDOM VALUES FROM A NORMAL DISTRIBUTION

If you ever wish to do simulations which require values from a normal distribution, the TI-83 Plus has a built-in function which will allow you to generate the random values you will need. For example, suppose you need 25 random values from a *standard* normal distribution (mean = 0, standard deviation =1

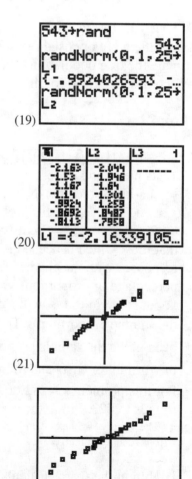

1. Set your seed to 543, so your answers will duplicate those seen here. See top of screen (19).
    543 [STO▸] [MATH] [◄] [1] [ENTER]

2. Next call the function randNorm from the MATH <Prb> submenu by pressing [MATH] [◄] [6]. You next need to specify the mean, the standard deviation and how many values you wish to generate. Fill in these as in the middle of screen (19) to generate 25 values from the standard normal <u>and</u> store them in L1. Press [ENTER].
    Repeat as in bottom of screen (19) this time storing in L2. Press [ENTER].

    (19)

3. Sort the data sets in L1 and L2, so you can look at the data as in screen (20). Note that the sets are different yet similar in distribution.

    (20)

4. Now setup StatPlot 1 for a normal quantile plot as in screen (17). Press [ZOOM] [9] for screen (21).
    Next, change the StatPlot 1 setup to plot the values from L2. Press [ZOOM] [9] for screen (22). You can see that the data generated in both runs is fairly normally distributed. You can try different sizes of data sets and different parameters (μ and σ) to get a feeling for the normal distribution.

    (21)

    (22)

6   Estimates and Sample Sizes

In this chapter you will learn how your TI-83 Plus calculator can aid you in estimating population parameters using the results of a single random sample. In this work, you will primarily use some of the options on the STAT Tests menu. You will learn how to estimate population proportions, means and variances as well as how to estimate the sizes of the samples you will need in each setting.

ESTIMATING A POPULATION PROPORTION

EXAMPLE Photo-Cop Survey Responses: 829 adult Minnesotans were surveyed, and 51% of them are opposed to the use of photo-cop for issuing traffic tickets. We wish to estimate the true population proportion. Find the margin of error E that corresponds to a 95% confidence level for the proportion. Then find the 95% confidence interval.

1-PropZInt

1. Press [STAT] [▶] [▶] [ALPHA] [MATH] to get to the STAT Tests menu and choose option A. You will see a screen like screen (1). Note that you need 3 inputs: x, n and C-level. In this problem it is obvious that n = 829 and C-level = 95. It is <u>important</u> to understand that the x which is needed is the <u>number</u> of responses with the characteristic of interest (<u>not</u> the percentage or proportion). Sometimes you are given x, but sometimes (as in this example) you are given the sample proportion $\hat{p}$. To find x when you have been given the sample proportion $\hat{p}$ you must use the formula $x = n\hat{p}$ and round to the nearest integer. For this problem $x = (829)(0.51) = 422.79$ which rounds to 423. Fill in the screen as in Screen (1).

   Note: The value of x <u>must</u> be an integer or else your TI-83 Plus will have a domain error.

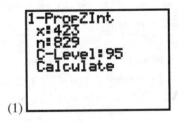

(1)

2. Highlight the word "Calculate" and press [ENTER]. You should see screen (2). The interval is given in parentheses. It is (.47622,.54428).

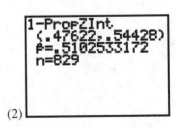

(2)

3. If you wish to find the margin of error E which was used to calculate this interval, you must find the

difference of the two endpoints of the interval and divide by 2. See screen (3). We find that the margin of error was E = .03403.

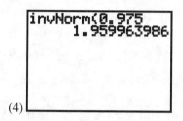
(3)

Home Screen Calculation for Proportion Estimates

Using the same example, you could calculate the margin of error and the confidence interval for the population proportion on your home screen.

1. You must find the value of $Z_{\alpha/2}$ for a 95% confidence level. To find this value, calculate as follows: $\alpha = 1-0.95 = 0.05$, $\alpha/2 = 0.05/2 = 0.025$. This means we need the value which separates the top 2.5% from the bottom 97.5% of the standard normal distribution. We use the InvNorm function as described in Chapter 5. See screen (4). We see the value needed is 1.96.

(4)

2. Now to calculate the value of the margin of error E use the formula $E = z_{\alpha/2}\sqrt{\dfrac{\hat{p}\hat{q}}{n}}$. We know from the problem that $\hat{p} = 0.51$, $\hat{q} = 0.49$ and n = 829. See calculations on screen (5). We have stored the margin of error as E.

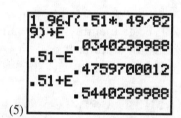
(5)

3. Now we continue in screen (5) to calculate the lower and upper endpoints of the confidence interval by taking our sample proportion $\hat{p} = 0.51$ and subtracting and adding E. We obtain nearly the same two interval endpoint values found when we used 1PropZInterval in screen (2).

Determining Sample Size Required to Estimate the Population Proportion

The formula for sample size is not built into the TI-83 Plus. We calculate it on the home screen. It is $n = (z_{\alpha/2})^2\,\hat{p}\hat{q}$ where $\hat{p} = 0.5$ if no other estimate is available.

EXAMPLE Sample Size for E-Mail Survey: Suppose a sociologist wants to determine the current percentage of U.S. households using e-mail. How many households must be surveyed in order to be 90% confident that the sample percentage is in error by no more than four percentage points?

a) Use the result from an earlier study which said 16.9% of U.S. households used e-mail.
b) Assume that we have no prior information suggesting a possible value of $\hat{p}$.

1. First find the critical z-value for 90% confidence. As explained on the previous page and seen in screen (6), we use InvNorm. We find the value is 1.645.

2. Screen (7) shows the calculations using the two formulas. We find that the sample size needs to be 238 if we use the prior estimate for $\hat{p}$ and 423 if we do not have a prior estimate and must use $\hat{p} = 0.5$.

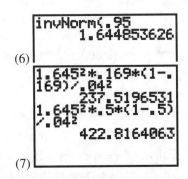

(6)

(7)

ESTIMATING A POPULATION MEAN: σ KNOWN

The formula for the confidence interval used to estimate the mean of a population when the standard deviation is known is built into the calculator and can be used via option 7 in the STAT Tests menu which is called ZInterval. This built-in function can be used with either raw data or summary statistics. The interval could also be calculated on the home screen in a similar manner as was shown for the confidence interval for a population proportion.

EXAMPLE Body Temperatures: For the sample of body temperatures in Data Set 4 of Appendix B, we have n = 106 and $\bar{x} = 98.2°F$. Assume the sample is random and that σ is somehow known to be 0.62°F. Using an 0.95 confidence level, find the margin of error and the confidence interval.

ZInterval with Summary Statistics

1. Press [STAT] [▶] [▶] [7] to get a screen similar to screen (8) for the ZInterval. Your first choice is the type of Input you will use. For this problem you have summary statistics (not raw data), so you should highlight on "Stats" and press [ENTER]. Now fill in all the other information which was given in your problem as you see it in screen (8).

2. Highlight the word "Calculate" and press [ENTER]. Now you should see screen (9) and your interval.

3. To retrieve the margin of error that was used to build the interval, we again must find the difference.

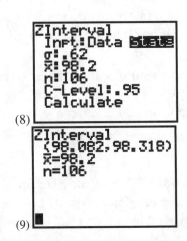

(8)

(9)

between the upper and lower endpoints of the interval and divide this difference by 2. See screen (10). The margin of error was 0.118°F.

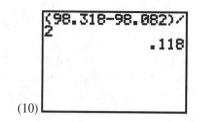

(10)

ZInterval with Raw Data

Using the Body Temperature example above, assume you do not yet have the sample statistics, but you do have the 106 body temperature values in Data Set 4 of Appendix B.

1. Put the data into list L1. (Do this by typing it in or transferring from another source.)

2. Press ⌊STAT⌋ ⌊▸⌋ ⌊▸⌋ ⌊7⌋ to get a screen for the ZInterval. Your first choice is the type of Input you will use. For this problem you have raw data, so you should highlight on "Data" and press ⌊ENTER⌋. Now fill in all the other information as in screen (11). Note that you must specify the standard deviation because it is supposed to be known and also the list where you have stored your data.

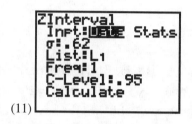

(11)

3. Highlight the word "Calculate" and press ⌊ENTER⌋. Now you should see screen (9) again since the outcome of the confidence interval is the same as when it was done with summary statistics.

Home Screen Calculations for Mean Estimates

To calculate the margin of error and confidence interval for the Body Temperature example on the home screen, we would first need to know the value of $Z_{\alpha/2}$ for a 95% confidence level. We already found this in screen (4) to be 1.96. Look at screen (12). Here, we used the formula $\bar{x} \pm E$ where $E = z_{\alpha/2}\dfrac{\sigma}{\sqrt{n}}$. We first calculated E,

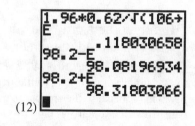

(12)

stored it as E and then used it to find the endpoints of the confidence interval for the mean temperature. Again, the interval is (98.082, 98.318).

Determining Sample Size Required to Estimate μ

The TI-83 Plus does not have a built-in function to calculate sample size. The formula can be calculated on the home screen. See the previous example of a sample size calculation for a proportion problem. Using the formula for sample size for a mean, proceed similarly.

ESTIMATING A POPULATION MEAN: σ NOT KNOWN

The formula for the confidence interval used to estimate the mean of a population when the standard deviation σ is not known is built into the calculator and can be used via option 8 in the STAT Tests menu which is called TInterval. This built-in function can be used with either raw data or summary statistics. The interval could also be calculated on the home screen in a similar manner as was shown for the other confidence intervals in this section.

EXAMPLE Body Temperatures: For the sample of body temperatures in Data Set 4 of Appendix B, we have n = 106 and $\bar{x}$ = 98.2°F. Assume the sample is random and that σ is <u>not</u> known, but we do have a value of s = 0.62°F which we can use as an estimate for σ. Using an 0.95 confidence level, find the margin of error and the confidence interval.

TInterval with Summary Statistics

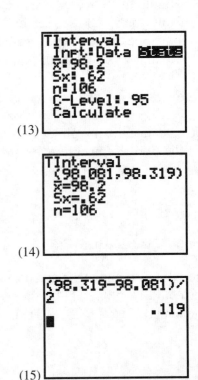

1. Press [STAT] [▶] [▶] [8] to get a screen similar to screen (13) for the TInterval. Your first choice is the type of Input you will use. For this problem you have summary statistics (not raw data), so you should highlight on "Stats" and press [ENTER]. Now fill in all the other information which was given in your problem as you see it in screen (13).

   (13)

2. Highlight the word "Calculate" and press [ENTER]. Now you should see screen (14). The 95% confidence interval is (98.081, 98.319).

   Note This interval varies <u>very</u> little from the ZInterval calculated earlier. This is because the sample size 106 is quite a large sample and the T distribution grows closer to the Z distribution as the sample size grows larger.

   (14)

3. To retrieve the margin of error that was used to build the interval, we again must find the difference between the upper and lower endpoints and divide this difference by 2. See screen (15). The margin of error was 0.119.

   (15)

TInterval with Raw Data

Using the Body Temperature example above, assume you do not yet have the sample statistics, but you do have the 106 body temperature values in Data Set 4 of Appendix B.

1. Put the data into list L1. (Do this by typing it in or transferring from another source.)

2. Press [STAT] [▶] [▶] [8] to get a screen for the TInterval. Your first choice is the type of Input you will use. For this problem you have raw data, so you should highlight on "Data" and press [ENTER]. Now fill in all the other information as in screen (16). This time you are not asked to specify σ because it is supposed to be unknown when using the TInterval. You must, of course, specify the list where you have stored the data.

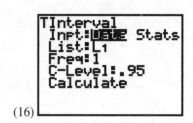

(16)

3. Highlight the word "Calculate" and press [ENTER]. Now you should see screen (14) again since the outcome of the confidence interval is the same as when it was done with summary statistics.

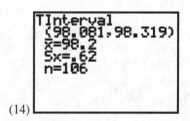

(14)

Home Screen Calculations for Mean Estimates

To calculate the margin of error for the above example on the home screen we would need To find the value of $t_{\alpha/2}$ for a 95% confidence level with (n-1) = 105 degrees of freedom.

Solving for Critical Values from the T Distribution

1. Press [MATH] [0] to get the Solver from the MATH menu. You should see a screen similar to screen (17). If your screen looks more like screen (18) use the [▲] key to cursor up. Next paste in the function "tcdf(" from the DISTR menu by pressing [2nd] [VARS] [5] .Fill in the rest of the values as in screen (17). (We are asking the calculator to find the value of X from the t distribution with 105 degrees of freedom which has an area of .025 to its right.)

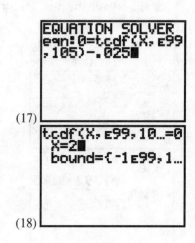

(17)

2. Press [ENTER] to see screen (18). Type 2 as the first guess for the prompt "x =."

(18)

3. With the cursor flashing on the X=2 line, press ALPHA ENTER (SOLVE). Then you must wait for the calculator to find X (which is the $t_{\alpha/2}$ value you desire.) Be patient – it takes quite a while! Finally, you should see screen (19) We find X = 1.9828.Once you have found the value of $t_{\alpha/2}$, the home screen calculation of the margin of error and confidence interval are very straight-forward. See screen (20) for the results.

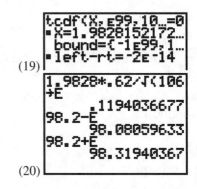

(19)

(20)

ESTIMATING A POPULATION VARIANCE

EXAMPLE   Body Temperatures: The data set of body temperatures is approximately bell-shaped with mean 98.2°F, s = 0.62°F, and n = 106. There are no outliers. Construct a 95% confidence interval estimate for σ, the standard deviation of the body temperature of the whole population.

With degrees of freedom (106-1) = 105, we can calculate the two critical values from the chi-square distribution which are required in this confidence interval calculation. We use the Solver as we did when finding critical t-values in screens (17), (18) and (19). See screens (21), (22), and (23) for the results for χ^2_L and screens (24), (25), and (26) for χ^2_R . These results can be used to calculate the confidence interval limits using the formula $\dfrac{(n-1)s^2}{\chi^2_R} < \sigma^2 < \dfrac{(n-1)s^2}{\chi^2_L}$. See screen (27) for the lower limit calculation and (28) for the upper limit. Our values are very close to the value obtained in the text, but more accurate as the text used *approximated* critical values.

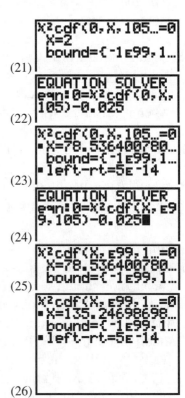

(21)

(22)

(23)

(24)

(25)

(26)

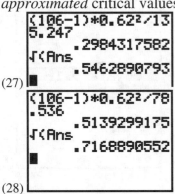

(27)

(28)

7   Hypothesis Testing

In this chapter, you will learn to use your TI-83 Plus to assist you in performing a variety of hypothesis tests based on one sample. You will see how to use the tests built into the STAT Tests menu as well as how to calculate test statistics on the home screen. You will be able to handle samples in the form of raw data as well as summary statistics. When performing a test you should always make sure that all assumptions are met. Refer to your main text for this material. There are many options available, so make sure you are following a routine which will allow you to include all steps required by your instructor in your write-up of a test.

TESTING A CLAIM ABOUT A PROPORTION

EXAMPLE   Survey of Drivers: Of 880 randomly selected drivers, 56% admitted that they run red lights. Based on these sample results, test the claim that more than half of all American drivers admit to running red lights, that is $p > 0.5$. We deduce that we are to test the following hypotheses: H_0: $p = 0.50$ H_1: $p > 0.50$.

1-PropZTest

We will use the built-in test for a population proportion from the STAT<Tests> menu. This is option 5, the 1-PropZTest. This test yields output which is perfectly-suited for the p-value method of testing a hypothesis.

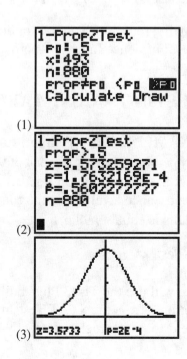

Press $\boxed{\text{STAT}}$ $\boxed{\triangleright}$ $\boxed{\triangleright}$ $\boxed{5}$ to call the 1-PropZTest from the STAT<Tests> menu and obtain a screen similar to screen (1). Look at the inputs which are required:
First is p_0, the value of the proportion *according to H_0*.
    This is 0.50 in our problem.
Second is the value of x, the number sampled with the
    characteristic of interest. We know that $x = n\,\hat{p} =$
    $(880)(0.56) = 492.8$ (must round up to 493).
Third is the value of n which is 880.
Fourth, we must choose the direction of our H_1. This is
    ">p_0" in our problem. Choices correspond to two-
    tailed, left-tailed and right-tailed tests.
Finally, we have the option of simply calculating our
    test results or obtaining a drawing of our results.
    Either choice will do.
Fill in the required inputs as in screen (1). If you choose "Calculate" and then press $\boxed{\text{ENTER}}$, you will see screen (2). If you choose "Draw" and then press $\boxed{\text{ENTER}}$, you will see screen (3).

(1)

(2)

(3)

Both displays on the previous page show us a test
statistic of Z = 3.5733 and a p-value of 2E⁻4 = .0002.

Note: In the Draw option, the picture of the distribution will show
the amount of *area* in the tail past your test statistics, which is
the p-value. In screen (3) we do not see any shaded area
because the p-value = .0002 is so small that there is not enough
for us to see anything.

Home Screen Calculations

You can calculate the test statistic on the home screen
using the formula $z = \dfrac{\hat{p} - p}{\sqrt{\dfrac{pq}{n}}} = \dfrac{0.56 - 0.5}{\sqrt{\dfrac{(0.5)(0.5)}{880}}}$. See screen

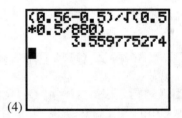

(4)

(4). We get z = 3.55977.

You can calculate the p-value of this test statistic by
finding the area (probability) in the tail of the standard
normal distribution past the statistic as in Chapter 5. See
the top of screen (5). Also (for those using the
Traditional Method) you can calculate the critical value
associated with a particular significance level (in this
case α = 0.05) as seen in the bottom of screen (5).

Note: The Traditional Method would lead us to compare the
critical value 1.645 and the test statistic 3.55977, finding that the
test statistic is greater and thus leading us to reject H_0 in favor of H_1
since this is a right-tailed (>) test.

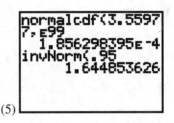

(5)

Finally, refer to Chapter 6 for details if you wish to use
the Confidence Interval Approach to testing.

TESTING A CLAIM ABOUT A MEAN, σ KNOWN

EXAMPLE Body Temperatures: Data Set 4 in Appendix B lists a sample of 106 body
temperatures having a mean of 98.2°F. Assume that the sample is a simple random sample
and that the population standard deviation σ is known to be 0.62°F. Use an α = 0.05
significance level to test the common belief that the mean body temperature of healthy
adults is equal to 98.6°F.

Z-Test

We will use the TI-83 Plus' built-in test for a population mean when σ is known. This is
option 1 from the STAT Tests menu. It is the Z-Test. As in the previous example, this test
yields output which is perfectly-suited for the p-value method of testing a hypothesis.

As before when you worked with confidence intervals for a mean, you have two options for input. You can input summary statistics or you can use the raw data as input. If you wish to use raw data, you must have it stored in a list. For our example below, we have stored the 106 body temperatures in list L1.

1. Press [STAT] [▶] [▶] [1] to get a screen similar to screen (6). If you choose to input "Data" and press [ENTER] your screen will be like screen (6). If your choice is to input "Stats" then your screen will look more like screen (7).

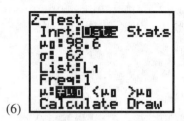

(6)

2. Note in both screens above, we had to specify the *hypothesized mean* $\mu_0 = 98.6$. We also had to specify the population variance σ because it is supposed to be known when using the Z-test. Whichever input form you are using, fill in these values as in screen (6) or (7).

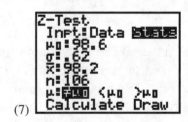

(7)

3. Fill in the rest of the information requested. You either need to tell the calculator where your data is as in screen (6) or give it the values of the summary statistics as in screen (7). Note this is a two-tailed test, so we choose $\neq\mu_0$ as our alternative hypothesis.

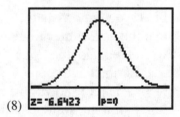

4. When all is filled in, choose either "Calculate" or "Draw" and [ENTER]. The results of "Draw" (this author's personal favorite option) are shown in screen (8).

(8)

Note: We get a test statistic of –6.6423 and a p-value of 0, so again we do not see any shaded area because the p-value is so small. Users of tables must remember to double the p-value and shade both tails when performing a two-tailed test, but calculator users need not do this because the calculator is programmed to automatically follow the proper procedures for a two-tailed test when the user chooses the two-tailed test option in the last line before entering.

Home Screen Calculation

See screen (9) for the home screen calculations for the test statistic $z = \dfrac{\bar{x} - \mu_0}{\dfrac{\sigma}{\sqrt{n}}}$ and it's p-value. Note we had to double the p-value to account for both tails. The p value is actually 3.104E⁻11 (essentially 0).

(9)

TESTING A CLAIM ABOUT A MEAN, σ NOT KNOWN

EXAMPLE Body Temperatures: A pre-med student in a statistics class obtains a simple random sample of 12 healthy adults. She measures their body temperatures and obtains the results listed below. Use a 0.05 significance level to test the claim that these body temperatures come from a population with a mean that is less than 98.6° F.

98.0   97.5   98.6   98.8   98.0   98.5   98.6   99.4   98.4   98.7   98.6   97.6

T-Test

We will use the TI-83 Plus' built-in test for a population mean when σ is not known. This is option 2 from the STAT<Tests> menu. It is the T-Test. As in the previous examples, this test yields output which is perfectly-suited for the p-value method of testing a hypothesis.

As in the preceding example, you have two options for input. You can input summary statistics or you can use the raw data as input. If you wish to use raw data, you must have it stored in a list. For this example, we do not have summary statistics, so we can begin by putting our 12 data values into L1.

1. First, you may wish to check to see if the assumption that the data comes from a normal population seems warranted. Do this by getting a normal quantile plot as described in Chapter 5. The results are in screen (10). The plot shows no extreme data values and is fairly straight, so we continue.

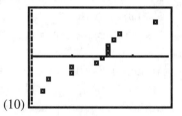

(10)

2. Press [STAT] [▶] [▶] [2] to get a screen similar to screen (11). Choose to input "Data" and press [ENTER].

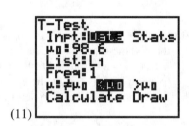

(11)

3. Specify the *hypothesized mean* $\mu_0 = 98.6$. This time we do not have to specify the population standard deviation σ because it is supposed to be unknown when using the T-test.

4. Fill in the rest of the information as in screen (11). You need to tell the calculator that the data is in L1. Note this is a left-tailed test, so we choose <μ_0 as our alternative hypothesis.

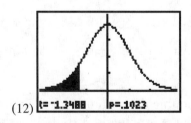

(12)

5. When all is filled in, choose either "Calculate" or "Draw" and [ENTER]. The results of "Draw" are shown in screen (12).

Note: We get a test statistic of t = ⁻1.3488 and a p-value of .1023. This time we see the shaded tail because this p-value is large enough for us to see something. It is also larger than 0.05, so we cannot reject H₀.

Home Screen Calculation

Once summary statistics for our data set are known., the T test statistic can be calculated on the home screen as was the Z statistic. Screens (13) and (14) show how to find the 0.05 critical value from the left-tail of a T distribution with 12-1=11 degrees of freedom. The use of the equation solver for this purpose was explained on page 49 of this guide. The test statistic ⁻1.3488 is larger than the critical value ⁻1.796. Since this is a left-tailed test, we would not be able to reject the null hypothesis.

(13)

(14)

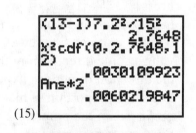

TESTING A CLAIM ABOUT A STANDARD DEVIATION OR VARIANCE

EXAMPLE IQ Scores of Statistics Professors: For a simple random sample of adults, IQ scores are normally distributed with mean 100 and standard deviation 15. A simple random sample of 13 statistics professors yields a standard deviation of s=7.2. Use a 0.05 significance level to test the claim that σ = 15. This is a two-tailed test.

1. Calculate the test statistic from the following

equation: $\chi^2 = (n-1)\dfrac{s^2}{\sigma^2} = (13-1)\dfrac{7.2^2}{15^2} = 2.7648$

as seen in the top of screen (15).

2. The bottom of screen (15) shows the calculation of the p-value of the test statistic using the χ^2cdf function located in the DISTR menu ([2nd] [VARS] [7]). Note, we doubled the p-value for this <u>two</u>-tailed test.

(15)

3. Finally, for those using the traditional method, screens (16) and (17) show the calculation of the lower critical value for this test.

The p-value is 0.006 which is certainly less than the significance level of the test. The test statistic (2.7648) is less than the left critical value of the test (4.484), so either way you look at it, the sample has provided evidence that the standard deviation of statistics professors is not equal to 15.

(16)

(17)

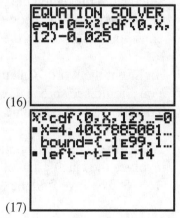

8   Inferences from Two Samples

In Chapters 6 and 7 you found confidence intervals and tested hypotheses for data sets that involved only one sample from one population. In this chapter you will learn how to extend the same concepts for use on data sets that involve two samples from two populations. As in Chapters 6 and 7 you will use functions from the STAT<Tests> menu. The presentation in this chapter assumes a familiarity with the materials presented in Chapters 6 and 7.

INFERENCES ABOUT TWO PROPORTIONS

EXAMPLE Racial Profiling: Using the sample data in Table 8-1 (repeated below) and a 0.05 significance level, test the claim that the proportion of black drivers stopped by the police is greater than the proportion of white drivers stopped.

	Black and Non-Hispanic	White and Non-Hispanic
Drivers Stopped by Police	24	147
Total Number observed	200	1400
Percent Stopped by Police	12.0%	10.5%

Hypothesis Test: **2-PropZTest**

1. Press [STAT] [▶] [▶] [6] to get to the STAT<Tests> menu and choose option 6, the *2-PropZTest*. You will see a screen like screen (1). The first four input values come directly from the table. Next we choose the direction of our test hypothesis. We are asked to test if the proportion of black drivers stopped is *greater than* the proportion of white drivers stopped. Since we represented the black drivers with x1 and n1, it would follow that our test hypothesis is p1>p2. Thus you should fill in the screen as in Screen (1).

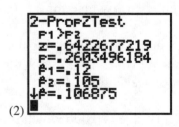
(1)

2. Highlight the word "Calculate" and press [ENTER]. You should see screen (2). The test statistic is z = 0.64227. Note the p-value is 0.2603.

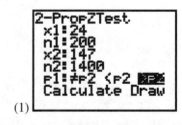
(2)

3. The Home screen calculation of the test statistic first involves the calculation of p = (x1+x2)/(n1+n2) = .16875. Then we find the test statistic

$Z = \dfrac{p1 = p2}{\sqrt{p(1-p)(\dfrac{1}{n1}+\dfrac{1}{n2})}}$. See screen (3). Again, we obtain

$Z = 0.64227.$

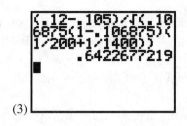

(3)

4. Since the p-value is greater than the significance level of 0.05, we find that our data has not provided us with significant evidence that the proportion of black drivers stopped by police is greater than that of white drivers. We cannot reject the null hypothesis.

Confidence Interval: 2-PropZInterval

EXAMPLE Racial Profiling: Use the sample data in Table 8-1 to construct a 90% confidence interval for the difference in the two population proportions.

1. Press [STAT] [▶] [▶] to get to the Stat<Tests> menu. Choose Option B which is the *2-PropZInterval*. Fill in the screen as in screen (4).

(4)

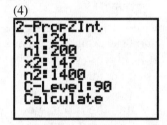

2. Highlight "Calculate" and press [ENTER] for screen (5). We obtain the results (−.0251, .05513). To retrieve the margin of error we can simply find the difference in the endpoints and divide by 2. E = (.05513−⁻.0251)/2 = .04.

3. The Home screen calculation is

$E = Z_{\alpha/2}\sqrt{\dfrac{p1*q1}{n1} + \dfrac{p2*q2}{n2}}$

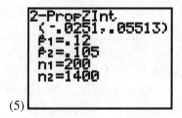

(5)

$= 1.645\sqrt{\dfrac{(.12)*(.88)}{200} + \dfrac{.(.105)*(.895)}{1400}}$

$=1.645\sqrt{(.12*.88/200+.105*.895/1400)} = 0.04.$

INFERENCES ABOUT TWO MEANS: INDEPENDENT SAMPLES

When you have a data set which is comprised of values from two independent samples of two populations it can at first seem difficult choosing how to begin. For the problems in your Triola text it is assumed that you do not know the values of the population variances σ_1^2 and σ_2^2. (In real life, this is almost always the case.) If you, in some future setting, know the values of the population variances you can use the *2SampZTest* and the *2SampZInterval* procedures (options 3 and 9 in your STAT<Tests> menu). With the idea of keeping things simple, we will not go into more detail or show examples on these procedures in this companion.

Hypothesis Testing: 2-SampTTest (Assuming $\sigma_1 \neq \sigma_2$)

EXAMPLE Bonds and McGwire Homerun Distances: Data Set 30 in Appendix B of your Triola textbook includes the distances of the homeruns hit in record-setting seasons by professional baseball players Mark McGwire and Barry Bonds. Use a 0.05 significance level to test the claim that the distances come from populations with *different* means.

Naturally, we must first get the Bonds and McGwire data into two separate lists in your calculator. (You can type the data in, transfer it from another calculator or bring it in from the APPS if you have the Triola Appendix data there.) We have placed the data in lists L1 and L2.

1. Press [STAT] [▶] [▶] [4] to choose Option 4 in the Stat<Tests> menu which is the 2-SampTTest. You will see a screen somewhat like screen (6). Since you have sets of raw data, highlight "Data" and [ENTER].

    (6)

    Note: If you had only been given summary statistics (as is the case in some textbook problems), you would highlight "Stats" and [ENTER]. Then you would be prompted to fill in all of the statistics for both data sets.

2. Match the inputs you see in screen (6). Note we are telling the TI-83 plus which lists contain our two data sets. Near the bottom of the screen we choose the direction of the test hypothesis. This is a *two-tailed* test because no direction was specified in the question. We were simply asked to test if the mean distances were *different*. Also in the very bottom of the screen, we have chosen the answer "No" to the question of whether or not we will *pool* our standard deviations. (For homework exercises 5-24 in your text, you are advised to <u>not</u> assume the standard deviations are equal. This equated to <u>not</u> pooling.).

    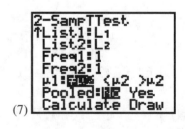
    (7)

3. Press the [▼] key to see the rest of the screen as in screen (7). You can choose either option "Calculate" or "Draw". We chose "Draw" and pressed [ENTER]. The result is screen (8). You can see the test statistic in the lower left corner is t=2.2788. The p-value of 0.0244 is displayed in the lower right corner. It follows that we have sufficient evidence at the 0.05 significance level that the mean distances of homeruns hit by Bonds and McGwire were different.

    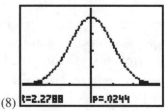
    (8)

Confidence Interval: **2-SampTInterval (Assuming $\sigma_1 \neq \sigma_2$)**

EXAMPLE Confidence Interval for Bonds and McGwire Homerun Distances: Again using the data sets from Data Set 30 in the Appendix, construct a 95% confidence interval estimate of the difference between the mean homerun distance of Mark McGwire and the mean homerun distance of Barry Bonds during their record-setting seasons.

The two data sets are stored in lists L1 and L2.

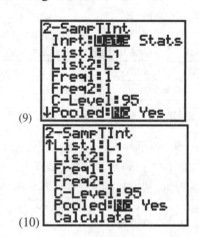

1. Press STAT ▶ ▶ 0 to choose Option 0 in the Stat<Tests> menu which is the 2-SampTInterval. You will see a screen somewhat like screen (9). You have sets of raw data, so highlight "Data and ENTER

(9)

    Note: If you had only been given summary statistics (as is the case in some textbook problems), you would highlight "Stats" and ENTER. Then you would be prompted to fill in all of the statistics for both data sets.

2. Fill in the rest of the information to duplicate what you see in screen (9). Note the near the bottom we indicate that our desired confidence level is 95%. Again, we answer "No" to the pooling question.

(10)

3. Press the ▼ key to see the rest of the screen as in screen (10). Then highlight "Calculate" and press ENTER. The result is screen (11). You can see the confidence interval is (1.947, 27.739). We are 95% confident that the difference in the mean homerun distances is between 1.9 and 27.7 feet (thus not likely to be zero.) We can find the margin of error by $E = (27.7-1.9)/2 = 12.9$ feet.

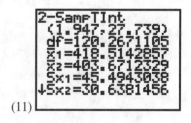

(11)

Hypothesis Testing and Confidence Intervals: (Assuming $\sigma_1 = \sigma_2$)

In problems 25-28 in section 8.3 of your text, you are told to assume the two independent samples came from normal populations with equal standard deviations ($\sigma_1 = \sigma_2$). In order to answer questions such as these, the only modification you should make to the above instructions is to answer "Yes" to the question of whether to pool or not. Your TI-83 plus will pool the two sample standard deviations and use the appropriate formulas for hypothesis test statistics and confidence intervals based on your instructions. In the end results, you will see the pooled standard deviation. It will be called Sxp.

INFERENCES ABOUT TWO MEANS: MATCHED PAIRS

EXAMPLE Are Forecast Temperatures Accurate: The table below consists of 5 actual low temperatures and the corresponding low temperatures that were predicted five days earlier. The data consists of matched pairs, because each pair of values represents the same day. The forecast temperatures appear to be very different from the actual temperatures, but is there sufficient evidence to conclude that the mean difference in not zero? Use a 0.05 significance level to test the claim that there is a difference between the actual low temperatures and the low temperatures that were forecast five dayx earlier.

Actual Low	1	-5	-5	23	9
Low Forecast 5 days earlier	16	16	20	22	15
Difference (Actual – Predicted)	-15	-21	-25	1	-6

We see that the above problem leads to the following hypotheses:
    H_0: $\mu_d = 0$ H_1: $\mu_d \neq 0$
Put the actual low temperatures in L1 and the predicted low temperatures in L2. Store the differences (L1-L2) in L3. Do this by highlighting L3 in the Statistics Editor (STAT 1) and then typing L1-L2 and pressing ENTER. The results should be the same as those seen in the bottom row of the above table. Now you are ready to treat the differences as a single data set on which you can perform the desired test.

1. Press STAT ▶ ▶ 2 so that you are choosing Option 2 on the Stat<Tests> menu which is the T-Test. Set up the resulting screen to match screen (12). Note that we are telling the TI-83 Plus that our data (the differences) is in L3. We are also specifying that the hypothesized mean μ_0 is 0 and that this is a two-tailed test.

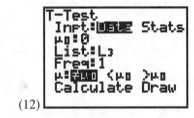

(12)

2. Highlight "Calculate" and press ENTER for screen (13). Note that the test statistic is t = ⁻2.762 and the p-value is 0.0507. This is larger than the significance level of 0.05, so our data was not strong enough evidence that there was an actual difference in the means. Also note that the values $\bar{x}$ and Sx are in this problem synonymous with $\bar{d}$ and Sd.

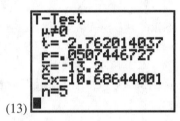

(13)

3. The test statistic can be calculated on the home screen by t = ($\bar{d}$ - μ_0)/(Sd/$\sqrt{n}$) = (⁻13.2 – 0)/(10.686/$\sqrt{(5)}$) = ⁻2.762.
    This, of course, would require your knowing the values of $\bar{d}$ and Sd. These could have been found using STAT ▶ 1 2nd 3 ENTER.

Confidence Interval for μ_d

EXAMPLE Are Forecast Temperatures Accurate?:   Use the same sample matched pairs to construct a 95% confidence interval estimate of μ_d which is the mean of the differences between actual low temperatures and five day forecast low temperatures.

1. Press STAT ▶ ▶ 8 to choose Option 8 of the Stat<Tests> menu which is the TInterval. Setup the screen as in screen (14).

```
TInterval
Inpt:DATA Stats
List:L₃
Freq:1
C-Level:95
Calculate
```
(14)

2. Highlight "Calculate" and press ENTER. You should see screen (15). The 95% confidence interval is given as (⁻26.47, .06897). Rounding, we can say we are 95% confidence that the mean difference in the actual and predicted low temperatures is between ⁻26.5 and 0.1 degrees. This implies that the mean difference could be 0 (because 0 is contained in the interval). Again, our sample has not given sufficient evidence that there is a difference in the means.

```
TInterval
(-26.47,.06897)
x̄=-13.2
Sx=10.68644001
n=5
```
(15)

3. The Home screen calculation of the margin of error of the above confidence interval would involve the formula $E = t_{\alpha/2} \dfrac{s_d}{\sqrt{n}} = 2.776 * 10.7 / \sqrt{5} = 13.3$. The value 2.776 is from the t-table with $(5-1) = 4$ degrees of freedom.

COMPARING VARIANCES IN TWO SAMPLES

The following procedure is used to test if there is a difference in the variances of two populations based on two independent samples drawn from the populations. This test is sometimes used to decide whether or not to pool the standard deviations when comparing two population means. If this test determines the variances (and thus the standard deviations) are different then one would not want to pool the standard deviations.

EXAMPLE   Coke Versus Pepsi: Data Set 17 in Appendix B includes the weights (in pounds) of samples of regular Coke and regular Pepsi. The sample statistics are summarized in the accompanying table. Use a 0.05 significance level to test the claim that the weights of regular Coke and regular Pepsi have the same standard deviation.

	Regular Coke	Regular Pepsi
n	36	36
$\overline{x}$	0.81682	0.82410
s	0.007507	0.005701

The above leads us to test the following hypotheses: $H_0: \sigma_1 = \sigma_2$ $H_1: \sigma_1 \neq \sigma_2$

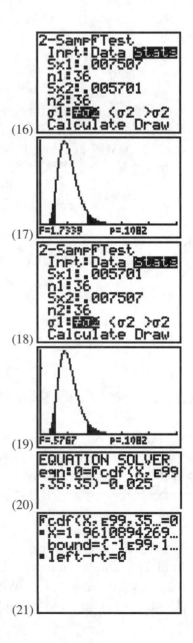

1. Press [STAT] [▶] [▶] [ALPHA] [x^{-1}]. This key sequence is choosing Option D in the Stat<Tests> menu which is the 2-SampFTest. Duplicate the screen you see in screen (16). (This time we are using the summary statistics instead of the raw data.)

2. If you choose to highlight "Draw" and press [ENTER], you will see screen (17). The test statistic is F = 1.7339 and the p-value is 0.1082.

3. In screen (18) we reverse the two data sets, so that we input the Pepsi set first. Screen (19) shows the results. We note that it changes the test statistic to F = 0.5767, but the p-value remains 0.1082. Since the p-value is greater than the significance level of 0.05, we cannot reject the null hypothesis. We do not have enough evidence to conclude that the standard deviations of the weights of Coke and Pepsi are not equal.

4. We conclude this chapter by illustrating the use of the Solver in finding the right-tail critical value of an F statistic. This is shown in screens (20) and (21) and is similar to the example on page 49 for T statistics. We see that our right-tail critical value is 1.9611. Since our test statistic was F = 1.7339, we are not in the critical region. Thus again, we could not reject the null hypothesis.

(16)

(17)

(18)

(19)

(20)

(21)

9   Correlation and Regression

In this chapter we will see how the TI-83 Plus can help with simple linear regression and correlation. The calculator has a few built-in functions to aid in this work, but the most useful all-around is option E on the Stat<Tests> menu which is the LinRegTTest. We will also study multiple regression. The TI-83 Plus does not have a built-in function for this process, so we will use a program called **A2MULREG** in this work.

SIMPLE LINEAR REGRESSION AND CORRELATION

EXAMPLE Boats and Manatees: Should boating restrictions be imposed to reduce the killing of manatees? The table below gives a sample of ten years of data. The x values are the number of registered Florida pleasure craft (in tens of thousands) and the y-values are the number of manatee deaths. We will use this data to study the relationship (if any) between these two variables.

x	68	68	67	70	71	73	76	81	83	84
y	53	38	35	49	42	60	54	67	82	78

Scatter Plot

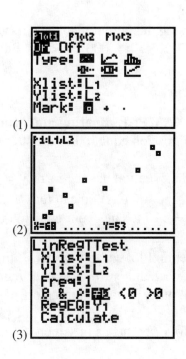

1. Enter the data into L1 and L2.

2. Set up Plot 1 for a scatter plot as in screen (1)

3. Press [ZOOM] [9] [TRACE] for the plot in screen (2).

The scatter plot seems to reveal a pattern indicating that more pleasure craft lead to more manatee deaths.

Linear Correlation Coefficient r

EXAMPLE Boating and Manatee Deaths: Using the data, find the value of the linear correlation coefficient r.

1. Press [STAT] [▶] [▶] [ALPHA] [SIN]. (You are choosing option E: LinRegTTest from the STAT<Tests> menu.) Set up the screen as in screen (3). Paste in the Y1 from [VARS] [▶] [1] [1].

2. Highlight Calculate in the last line and press ENTER
for the two screens of output (4) and (5). Note that
the last line of screen (5) gives r = .9215229234.

Note: There are other ways of calculating r on the TI-83 Plus, but
this method is more useful all around as it provides a lot of
other results of interest.

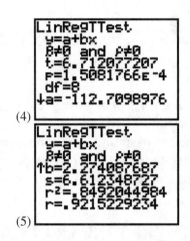

(4)

(5)

Explained Variation r^2 (Coefficient of Determination)

EXAMPLE Boating and Manatees: Referring to the
boating/manatee deaths data, what proportion of the
variation in manatee deaths can be explained by the
variation in the number of pleasure crafts?

In the second to last line of screen (5) we see that r^2 =
.8492, so about 85% of the variation in manatee deaths
can be explained by the variation in the number of
pleasure crafts.

Formal Hypothesis Test of the Significance of r

EXAMPLE Boating and Manatees: Using the data above, test the claim that there is
significant linear correlation between the number of registered pleasure crafts and the
number of manatee deaths. . Thus test H_0: $\rho = 0$ versus H_1: $\rho \neq 0$.

Using the output displayed in screen (4), we see the test statistic t = 6.712 and the p-value
= 1.508E-4 = .000150 < .05, indicating significant positive linear correlation.

Regression

EXAMPLE Boating and Manatees: For the data we have been working with, find the
regression equation of the straight line that relates x and y.

The equation has the form $\hat{y} = b_0 + b_1 x$. Your calculator uses the form $\hat{y} = a + bx$, so a =
b_0 and b = b_1. You can look at the output on screens (4) and (5) and see that a = -112.7 and
b = 2.274. Thus your equation is $\hat{y} = -112.7 + 2.274x$.

Set up Plot1 as in screen (1). In screen (3) you instructed
the calculator to place your regression equation in Y1. If
all other plots are turned off, you can press ZOOM 9 and
TRACE for the regression line plotted through the scatter
plot of points as in screen (6).

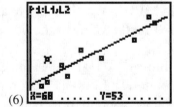

(6)

Predictions

EXAMPLE Boating and Manatees: Using the sample data, you found that there is a significant linear correlation between the number of registered pleasure crafts and the number of manatee deaths. You also found the regression equation. Now suppose that in the year 2001 there were 850,000 registered boats. Use the regression equation to predict the number of manatee deaths from boats that year. First note that 850,000 boats corresponds to an x-value of 85 since x was the number of boats in tens of thousands.

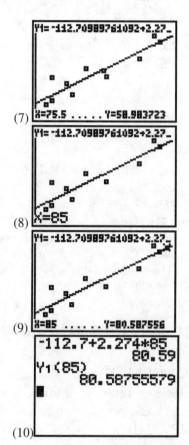

1. With the regression line and scatter plot displayed as in screen (6) press ▾ to hop from a data point to the regression line similar to screen (7).

2. **T**ype in 85. A large X=85 will show in the bottom line as in screen (8). Press ENTER for screen (9). We see the predicted y value is 80.6 or nearly 81 manatee deaths.

You can also calculate the predicted y on the Home screen by typing in the regression equation as in the top line of screen (10) or by pasting Y1 (VARS ▸ 1 1) to the Home screen and then typing (85) and pressing ENTER, as in the last line of screen (10).

(7)

(8)

(9)

(10)

Prediction Intervals

EXAMPLE   Boating and Manatees: For the paired boat/manatee data, we just found that the best prediction for x = 85 (850,000 registered boats) is y = 80.6 manatee deaths. Find a 95% prediction interval for the number of manatee deaths if the number of boats is 850,000.

The only way to do this is to calculate the interval on the Home screen using the formula. From Table A-3 of the text, we find the value $t_{\alpha/2} = 2.306$ using 10-2 = 8 degrees of freedom. The other quantities needed in the formula will be stored in the calculator after you have performed the LinRegTTest. You can paste them in from the VARS menu as described below.

1. First in screen (11) we store 85 as X, 2.306 as T and Y1(X) as Y. Here Y1(X) is the value we get when we input X=85 into the regression equation stored in Y1. We separate the different values with colons.

(11)

2. Press ENTER to reveal the prediction value 80.6

3. Lines 4, 5, and 6 of screen (11) show the calculation of the margin of error E using the formula from the text. Values used in the formula are stored in the Statistics submenu of the VARS menu. You can find and paste in:

(11)

s at VARS 5 ▶ ▶ ▶ 0 (in the Test menu)
n at VARS 5 1 (in the XY menu)
$\bar{x}$ at VARS 5 2 (in the XY menu)
Σx^2 at VARS 5 ▶ 2 (in the Σ menu)
and Σx at VARS 5 ▶ 1 (in the Σ menu)
Press ENTER to reveal that E = 18.12

Note: As you work, look carefully at the quantities in the statistics submenus, so you can familiarize yourself with what is available to you and where it is located.

4. In screen (12) we start with our prediction value Y and add and subtract the margin of error to form the 95% confidence interval 62.47<y<98.71.

(12)

Note: The prediction interval for different x-values and different confidence levels can be easily calculated using the last-entry feature (2nd ENTER). Simply recall the top input lines of screen (11) and change the inputs as needed and press ENTER. Then recall the equation to calculate E.

MULTIPLE REGRESSION

EXAMPLE Bears: Measurements taken from a set of 8 bears are given below and in Table 9-3. Find the multiple regression equation in which the dependent (y) variable is weight and the independent variables are head length (HEADL) and total overall length (LENGTH).

Y or C1 WEIGHT	C2 AGE	C3 HEADL	C4 HEADW	C5 NECK	C6 LENGTH	C7 CHEST
80	19	11	5.5	16	53	26
344	55	16.5	9	28	67.5	45
416	81	15.5	8	31	72	54
348	115	17	10	31.5	72	49
262	56	15	7.5	26.5	73.5	41
360	51	13.5	8	27	68.5	49
332	68	16	9	29	73	44
34	8	9	4.5	13	37	19

The TI-83 Plus does not have built-in multiple regression features. We will use a program written for this purpose called A2MULREG. This program comes on the CD-ROM which accompanies your text. See the Appendix for details. Program A2MULREG requires that the data set be stored in matrix [D] on your TI-83 Plus. We will walk through this process below. One important restriction is that the dependent variable (y) must be stored in the first column of [D]. This is not the case when using most statistical software such as Minitab.

Entering Data into Matrix [D]

The data can be imported from another TI-83 Plus or from a computer. The following method is for entering the data from a keyboard. Press [2nd] [x⁻¹] [▶] [▶] to call the MATRIX menu and to choose the EDIT submenu. Go down the screen to highlight [D] and press [ENTER] [8] [ENTER] [7] [ENTER] for screen (13). You have just instructed the calculator that [D] will have 8 rows and 7 columns of data. (There are 8 bears with 7 variables for each.) You may have different values in your matrix [D], but leave them for now as we will type over them.

(13)

Now enter the data row by row. Start with the cursor in the first row, first column. Type each data set value from Table 9.3 and press [ENTER] after each. You will end by seeing screen (14).

(14)

With the data stored in [D], we now use the program A2MULREG to verify the Minitab output given in the text for the three most important components:

1. The multiple regression equation is given as
    WEIGHT = -374 + 18.8HEADL + 5.87LENGTH

2. Adjusted R^2 = 0.759

3. The overall significance of the regression equation is
    p = 0.012.

Program A2MULREG

1. Press [PRGM] and use [▼] to highlight A2MULREG. Press [ENTER] for screen (15). Then press [ENTER] again for screen (16).

(15)

(16)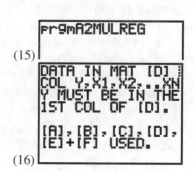

2. Press ENTER for screen (17) which gives you 3 options. Press 1 for MULT REGRESSION.

3. The next step requires you to fill in requested information as in screen (18). You are asked for the number of independent variables (2) and for the columns in matrix [D] where these variables are stored. (columns 3 and 6). Fill in this information.

4. Press ENTER after inputting the "6" and you should get screen (19). You can see that the p-value is .012 and the Adjusted R^2 value (ADJ) is .7592 thus confirming the Minitab results.

5. Press ENTER for screen (20). The value B0 is the constant from the regression equation. The COEFF values are the two coefficients for the independent random variables (HEADL and LENGTH). We come up with the regression equation
WEIGHT=¯374.3+18.820HEADL+5.875LENGTH

6. Press ENTER for screen (21) and choose option 4 which is to quit.

Correlation Matrix

EXAMPLE: What is the best regression equation if only a single independent variable is to be used?

1. When you ran Program A2MULREG, screen (17) gave you the option of calculating the correlation matrix. Begin running the program again. This time highlight the option of calculating the correlation matrix as seen in screen (22).
Note: Pressing ENTER from the Home screen will restart the program if the last thing done was to quit it.

2. Press 2 and wait patiently as this calculation takes some time. The partial output is given in screen (23). Looking at just the first column, we can see that the last of the variables, CHEST, has the greatest linear correlation with the first variable WEIGHT (r = .992). Thus it is the best single variable to use in a regression since its r^2 = .983.

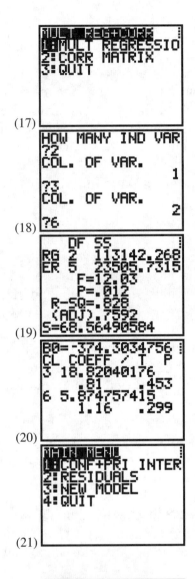

(17)

(18)

(19)

(20)

(21)

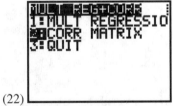

(22)

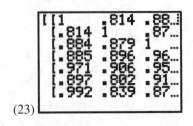

(23)

10 Multinomial Experiments and Contingency Tables

In this chapter we will use the TI-83 Plus STAT Editor as a spreadsheet to calculate the χ^2 test statistic used in the goodness of fit test for multinomial experiments. We will also use a built-in test (option C in the STAT<Tests> menu) to do contingency table analysis.

MULTINOMIAL EXPERIMENTS: GOODNESS OF FIT TESTS

EXAMPLE Detecting Fraud: Refer to the table below which is a recreation of part of Table 10-1 in your text. It contains a frequency analysis of the leading digits on 784 checks. Test the claim that the digits do not occur with the frequency stipulated by Benford's Law. Use significance level $\alpha = 0.01$.

Lead digit	1	2	3	4	5	6	7	8	9
Expected % Frequency	30.1	17.6	12.6	9.7	7.9	6.7	5.8	5.1	4.6
Observed Frequency	0	15	0	76	479	183	8	23	0

Calculating χ^2 Statistic $\Sigma[(O - E)^2/E]$

1. Put the observed frequencies into L1 and the expected proportions into L3.

2. Highlight L2 as at the top of screen (1) and type L3*sum(L1 as in the bottom of the screen (Find "sum(" at [2nd] [STAT] [▶] [▶] [5].)

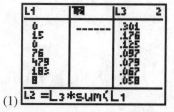
(1)

3. Press [ENTER] for the expected frequencies (E) in L2 as in screen (2). (If these values are given or are easy to calculate, you can simply enter them into L2.)

4. Highlight L4 and type (L1-L2)^2/L2 as in the last line of screen (2). Press [ENTER] for the contribution made by each of the digits to the overall chi-square statistic as in screen (3). We can see that the largest contributions is made by 5.

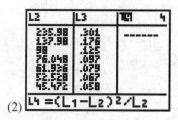
(2)

5. Press 2nd MODE to Quit and return to the Home Screen. Sum the elements of L4, as in screen (4). We see the chi-square statistic is 3650.2514.

Computing the p-value of the χ^2 Statistic

6. Press 2nd VARS 7 to paste "χ^2cdf(" on the screen. Then type 3650.2514,E99,8 and press ENTER for a p-value as in screen (5). (You have asked for the probability of a test statistic greater than 3650.2514 in a chi-square distribution with df = 8.)

7. Since the p-value is essentially 0 and much smaller than the significance level $\alpha = 0.01$, we would reject the hypothesis that the lead digits follow Benford's Law and reason that the discrepancy could be proof of fraud

    To graphically compare the observed frequencies with the expected frequencies, put the integers 1 to 9 in L6 as in screen (6).

    Set up Plot1 and Plot2 as in screen (7). As illustrated, use a different mark for the observed frequencies in L1 and the expected frequencies in L2. Press ZOOM 9 TRACE for screen (8).

Note: The observed proportions and expected proportions could have been plotted as in Figure 10.6(a) of the text, but the graph would look the same-only the y-axis scale would change.

CONTINGENCY TABLES

The examples in this section refer to the table below which summarizes the fate of the passengers and crew when the Titanic sank on April 15, 1912. The text advises we "stipulate that the data are sample data randomly selected from the population of all theoretical people who would find themselves in the same conditions…" for the purpose of this analysis.

	Men	Women	Boys	Girls	Total
Survived	332 (20%)	318 (75%)	29 (45%)	27 (60%)	706 (32%)
Died	1360 (80%)	104 (25%)	35 (55%)	18 (40%)	1517 (68%)

EXAMPLE Titanic Expected Frequency: Find the expected frequencies for the lower-left cell, assuming independence between the row variable (whether the person survived) and the column variable (whether the person was a man, woman, boy or girl).

The output using the built in chi-square test for independence will automatically give all expected values. To calculate this one by hand, we would calculate
E=(row total)*(column total)/(grand total)
= (1360+104+35+18)*(332+1360)/(332+318+29+27+1360+104+35+18) = 1154.64.

EXAMPLE Titanic Sinking: At the 0.05 significance level, use the data in the table to test the claim that when the Titanic sank, whether someone survived or died was independent of whether the person is a man, woman, boy or girl.

1. Enter the data in a matrix. We use matrix [A] for this example. Press [2nd] [x^{-1}] [▶] [▶] [ENTER] to call the MATRX menu and Edit matrix [A]. Then press [2] [ENTER] [4] [ENTER] to set the size of [A] as in screen (9). You might have values other than 0 in your matrix [A], but leave them for now as we will type over them.

Note: If your previous matrix [A] had more than one digit for the number of rows or columns, you will have to delete the second digit with [DEL].

(9)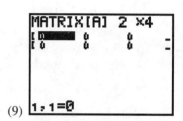

2. Type the table frequency entries into the matrix as in screen (10). Press [ENTER] after each entry.

(10)

3. Press [STAT] [▶] [▶] [ALPHA] [PRGM] to choose option C from the STAT<Tests> menu. This is C: χ^2-Test. Duplicate screen (11) by pasting in matrix [A] from the MATRX<NAMES> menu with [2nd] [x^{-1}] [1]. Similarly paste in matrix [E] with [2nd] [x^{-1}] [5].

(11)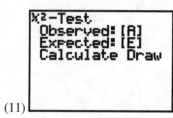

4. Highlight "Calculate" in the last line of screen (11) and press [ENTER] for screen (12). Note the test statistic is 507.08 with a p-value of 0. Since the p-value is less than the significance level (0.05) of the test, we reject the null hypothesis. It appears that whether a person survived the Titanic and whether the person was a man, woman, boy or girl were dependent.

(12)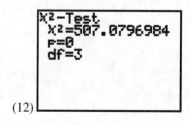

As mentioned previously, the expected cell frequencies are automatically calculated when the test is run and are stored in matrix [E]. To compare the values in matrices [A] and [E] on the same screen, first press MODE and make the resulting screen look like screen (13). This will change the display to show 0 decimal places. Press 2nd MODE to Quit and return to the Home screen. (Do not forget to change the MODE back to Float when you are finished with this exercise.)

(13)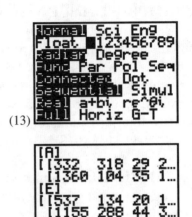

Paste [A] to the Home screen and press ENTER. Do the same for [E]. You should see screen (14).

Notice that 332 men survived when 537 were expected to survive according to the null hypothesis. Also 318 women survived when only 134 were expected to survive. These appear to be significantly different values and in fact were determined to be so by the hypothesis test performed earlier.

(14)

11 Analysis of Variance

In this chapter we will use the TI-83 Plus built-in function for doing one-way ANOVA problems. This function is option F on the STAT<Tests> menu. We will use a program called A1ANOVA to extend our capabilities to do two-way ANOVA problems for two factor designs with equal numbers of observations in each cell. The output for this program matches the Minitab ANOVA tables in the text. See the text for the proper interpretation for these tables.

ONE-WAY ANOVA

EXAMPLE Readability of Clancy, Rowling and Tolstoy: Given the readability scores summarized in Table 11-1 in the text and a significance level of $\alpha = 0.05$, use the TI-83 Plus calculator to test the claim that the three samples came from populations with means that are not all the same. The data referred to are the Flesch Reading Ease scores. The actual data values are found in Data Set 14 of the Appendix and in the table below.

Clancy L1	58.2 73.4 73.1 64.4 72.7 89.2 43.9 76.3 76.4 78.9 69.4 72.9
Rowling L2	85.3 84.3 79.5 82.5 80.2 84.6 79.2 70.9 78.6 86.2 74.0 83.7
Tolstoy L3	69.4 64.2 71.4 71.6 68.5 51.9 72.2 74.4 52.8 58.4 65.4 73.6

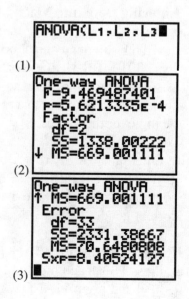

1. Put the data in lists L1 to L3 as indicated in the table. (You can import from the Data Apps.)

2. Press [STAT] [▶] [▶] [ALPHA] [COS] to choose option F on the STAT<Tests> menu and paste "ANOVA(" on the Home screen. Type L1 , L2 , L3 as in screen (1).

3. Press [ENTER] for screens (2) and (3). We see the test statistic F = 9.469 and the p-value = 0.000562 just as seen in the text.

Note: The program A1ANOVA, introduced in the next section, gives the means and standard deviations of the raw data stored in the lists. The program also accepts sample summary statistics (means, standard deviations, and sample sizes) as an input option in addition to the raw data option. The TI-89 also accepts summary statistics and has the capability to perform two-way ANOVA.

TWO-WAY ANOVA

The following example uses program A1ANOVA to perform two-way ANOVA. The availability of A1ANOVA is given in the Appendix.

Two-Factor Design with an Equal Number of Observations per Cell

EXAMPLE Time in Seconds for New York Marathon Runners: The data used to illustrate the two-way ANOVA procedure in this chapter was randomly selected from Data Set 8 in Appendix B. It is partitioned into six categories according to two factors, gender and age. There are five observations in each of the categories. The data is duplicated below. Each column and row factor has been assigned a numerical value for use in our analyses. We will use this data to show how the TI-83 Plus (via the program A1ANOVA) can duplicate the two-way ANOVA results given in the text.

	Age 21-29 = 1	Age 30-39 =2	Age 40 and over =3
Male=1	13615 18784 14256 10905 12077	14677 16090 14086 16461 20808	14528 17034 14935 14996 22146
Female=2	16401 14216 15402 15326 12047	15357 16771 15036 16297 17636	17260 25399 18647 15077 25898

The data in the table above will be stored in matrix [D] with 30 rows and 3 columns. The data values are all in the first column. The second column identifies the gender associated with each data value (1=male, 2=female). The third column of [D] identifies the age class associated with the value. Here are the step by step instructions.

1. **Entering Data into Matrix [D]**
   (a) Press [2nd] [x⁻¹] [▶] [▶] [4] to call the MATRX menu, the EDIT submenu and choose matrix [D] to edit. Type 30 [ENTER] 3 [ENTER] for 30 rows and 3 columns as seen at the top of screen (4). Your matrix may not contain all zeroes, but that is fine as we will be typing over the values.

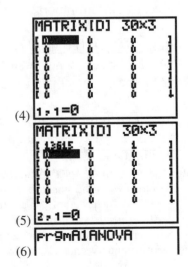

   (b) Enter data row by row. Begin with 13615 [ENTER] 1 [ENTER] 1 [ENTER] as in screen (5). Then continue typing in all the data values with their correct gender and age identifier.

2. **Running Program A1ANOVA**
   (a) Press [PRGM] and highlight A1ANOVA. Press [ENTER] and prgmA1ANOVA is pasted to the Home screen as in screen (6).

(b) Press ENTER for screen (7). Press ③ to choose option 3, the 2WAY FACTORIAL. You will then see screen (8) which is an instructional screen.

(c) Press ENTER for screen (9. This gives you two options: CONTINUE or QUIT. You could quit if the data were not already in matrix [D] as required.

(d) Press ① to continue since our data is stored in [D]. The result is the ANOVA table shown in screen (10) Press ENTER for screen (11).

The results for gender are $F(A) = 1.69$ with p-value 0.206. For age class $F(B) = 5.10$ with p-value 0.014. The interaction is given as $F(AB) = 1.17$ with p-value 0.329. These agree with the Minitab results shown in the text. Mean squares (MS) are not shown but can easily be calculated by dividing sum of squares (SS) by degrees of freedom (DF).

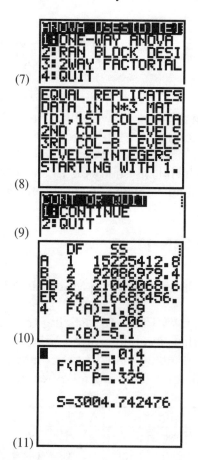

(7)

(8)

(9)

(10)

(11)

Special Case: One Observation per Cell and No Interaction

EXAMPLE Time in Seconds for New York Marathon Runners: As an example assume we have only the first entry in each cell of the table on the previous page. We thus have only 6 data values (one for each gender and age class combination). We will not be able to determine an effect due to interaction with only one value per cell, but we can perform two-factor ANOVA and duplicate the text's Minitab results.

Proceed by placing the six data values into matrix D which will this time be a 6 row, 3 column matrix.

Run program A1ANOVA as before. The results are shown in screens (12) and (13) and are similar to the Minitab output displayed in the text.

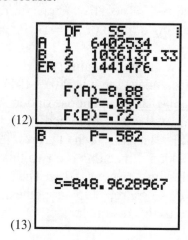

(12)

(13)

12   Nonparametric Statistics

In this chapter we will use the TI-83 Plus spreadsheet to perform most of the calculations. Examples will be given for each nonparametric test covered in your text. In some circumstances, when sample sizes are too large for the tables in your text, a test statistic z which is normally distributed can be calculated. The p-value of such a statistic can then be found using the normalcdf function. This process will be illustrated.

SIGN TEST

Claims Involving Matched Pairs

EXAMPLE   Measuring Intelligence in Children: The following data was obtained when 15 children were asked to build a block tower. The data is the time (in seconds) needed to build the tower in two different trials. Use a 0.05 significance level to test the claim that there is no difference between the times in the first and second trials.

Child	A	B	C	D	E	F	G	H	I	J	K	L	M	N	O
First trial	30	19	19	23	29	178	42	20	12	39	14	81	17	31	52
Second trial	30	6	14	8	14	52	14	22	17	8	11	30	14	17	15
Sign of difference	0	+	+	+	+	+	+	-	-	+	+	+	+	+	+

We let n = 14 (disregarding the 0 difference). If the times for the two trials were equal then the number of positive and negative differences would be approximately equal (14/2 = 7 each), but in the above table there are only 2 negative differences. Is this significantly different than what we expect? If the two trials are equal the distribution of the number of positive (or negative) signs for the differences would be binomial with n = 14 and p = 0.5 yielding a mean of np = 14*0.5 = 7. (You can review the binomial distribution in Ch. 4.)

We want the probability of having 2 or fewer negative differences which is P(0) + P(1) + P(2). Press 2nd VARS ALPHA MATH to choose option A from the VARS menu. This will paste "binomcdf(" on your screen. Fill in the 14,0.5,2 as in screen (1). Press ENTER to see the p-value of .0065. Since this is a two-tailed test, multiply this p-value by 2 (we get .013). The p-value is smaller than 0.05, so we reject the hypothesis that the times for the two trials are equal.

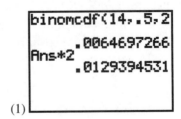
(1)

Claims Involving Nominal Data

EXAMPLE Gender Discrimination: A company acknowledges that about half the applicants for new jobs were men and half were women. All applicants met the basic job-qualification standards. Test the null hypothesis that men and women are hired equally by this company if of its last 100 hires only 30 were men.

H_0: $p = 0.5$ H_1: $p \neq 0.5$

This is a binomial distribution with n = 100 and p = 0.5. We wish to find the probability of having 30 or fewer men in such a situation. This is P(0) + P(1) + ... + P(30).

In screen (2) we paste up the binomcdf function and input 100, 0.5, 30. After we ENTER we find the one-tail p-value is 0.00003925. We double this for the two-tailed test to obtain 0.0000785. Since the p-value is smaller than 0.05, there is enough evidence to reject the claim that the hiring practices are fair.

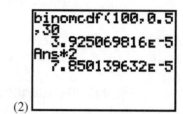

(2)

Claims about the Median of a Single Population

EXAMPLE Body Temperatures: Use the sign test to test the claim that the median value of the 106 body temperatures of healthy adults is less than 98.6°F. We are thus testing H_1: median < 98.6   versus H_0: median ≥ 98.6

The data set has 68 subjects with temperatures below 98.6°F, 23 subjects with temperatures above 98.6°F and 15 subjects with temperatures equal to 98.6°F. (We will later present steps for how to find these values.)

Discounting the 15 temperatures equal to 98.6°F because they do not add any information to this problem, the sample size is n = 68 + 23 = 91. If the median were 98.6, we would expect about half of these 91 values to be below the median and half to be above it. This is a binomial distribution with mean = n*p = 91*0.5 = 45.5.We want the probability of having 23 or fewer values above the median (as this is what has occurred).

Press 2nd VARS ALPHA MATH to choose option A from the VARS menu. This will again paste "binomcdf(" on your screen. Fill in the 91,0.5,23 as in screen (3). Press ENTER to see the p-value = 0.00000126. With such a small p-value there is good evidence that there are fewer temperatures above 98.6 than would be expected if it were the median. This supports the claim that the median is less than 98.6.

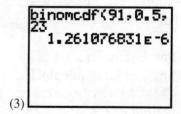

(3)

If the 106 body temperatures are saved in a list (e.g., L1), the following steps show one way the numbers below and above the hypothesized median could be obtained.

1. With your data in L1, highlight L2 at the top as in
   screen (4). Type L1 – 98.6 as in the bottom of screen
   (4). Press ENTER to see screen (5). We see some
   differences are negative, some are positive and some
   are 0.

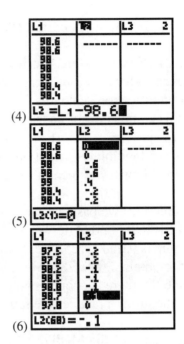

(4)

(5)

(6)

2. Press STAT 2 for the SortA(option from the STAT
   menu. Press 2nd 2 to choose L2 for sorting. Then
   press ENTER. The values will be sorted in ascending
   order when you go back to the editor with STAT 1.

3. Use the ▼ key to look at the sorted values. You will
   see that 68 values are below 98.6 (the differences are
   negative as in screen (6)). You will also find 15
   values equal to 98.6 (the differences are 0) and 23
   values above 98.6 (the differences are positive.)
   These are the numbers given earlier.

WILCOXON SIGNED RANK TEST FOR MATCHED PAIRS

EXAMPLE Measuring Intelligence in Children: The following data are repeated from
the first example in this chapter. We will use the Wilcoxon signed-ranks test to test the
claim of no difference between times on the two trials. We use significance level $\alpha = 0.05$.

Child	A	B	C	D	E	F	G	H	I	J	K	L	M	N	O
First trial	30	19	19	23	29	178	42	20	12	39	14	81	17	31	52
Second trial	30	6	14	8	14	52	14	22	17	8	11	30	14	17	15
Sign of difference	0	+	+	+	+	+	+	–	–	+	+	+	+	+	+

The following steps show a method for finding the sum of the positive ranks and the sum
of the absolute values of the negative ranks.

1. Put the first trial times in L1 and the second trial
   times in L2. Omit any 0 differences (in this case,
   Child A). Highlight L3 and type L1–L2 on the
   bottom line. Press ENTER to calculate the differences
   as in screen (7).

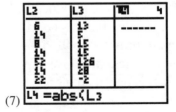

(7)

2. Highlight L4 and enter abs(L3, as in the bottom line
   of screen (7). (You can paste in "abs(" with MATH ▶

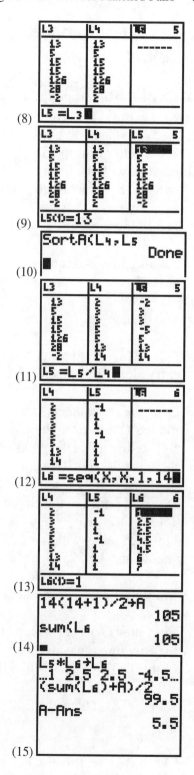

1.) Press ENTER for screen (8). Now L4 contains all positive values.

3. Copy the differences in L3 into L5 by highlighting L5, entering L3 (as in the bottom line of screen (8)), and then press ENTER for screen (9).

4. Press STAT 2 to paste "SortA(" on the screen as in screen (10). Then enter L4, L5 and press ENTER to see "Done". You have sorted L4 and carried the contents of L5 along. Press STAT 1 to return to the STAT editor as in screen (11).

5. Highlight L5 and enter L5 ÷ L4 for the last line of screen (11). Press ENTER for a column of positive and negative ones as in screen (12).

6. Generate the integers from 1 to 14 in L6. Do so by highlighting L6 and typing 2nd STAT ▶ 5. This chooses the seq option from the LIST<Ops> menu. Type X,X,1,14 as in the bottom of screen (12). Press ENTER, then modify L6 as in screen (13). You must place the rank of each value in L4 into L6. Account for items with tied ranks by averaging the ranks. For example the second and third values in L4 are both 3. They each receive a rank of (2+3)/2 = 2.5.

7. Quit and return to the Home screen. Type 14(14+1)/2 STO▶ ALPHA MATH ENTER for the sum of the ranks (105) to be stored as A. Sum the elements in L6 with 2nd STAT ▶ ▶ 5 2nd 6 ENTER. This too should be 105. If not, then recheck your ranks in L6. See screen (14).

8. Multiply L5∗L6 and store in L6 as in the top of screen (15). This puts a sign on the rankings in L6. Only the first and fourth ones in the list are negative.

9. (sum(L6)+A)/2 ENTER for 99.5 the sum of the positive ranks. Type A – 2nd (-) for 5.5 the sum of the negative ranks. We use the smaller value (5.5) for comparison with the appropriate value from the table in the text. (Table A-8). We find it is less than the critical value (21) and thus we can reject H_0.

WILCOXON RANK-SUM TEST FOR TWO INDEPENDENT SAMPLES

EXAMPLE Rowling and Tolstoy Data Set 14 in Appendix B of your text includes Flesch reading scores from each of two books by the above named authors. As explained in the book, the data was slightly modified by adding a 71.4 to the Rowling list in order to provide a better example for the Wilcoxon rank-sum test. Use the two sets of independent sample data with a 0.05 significance level to test the claim that reading scores from the two books have the same distribution.

The following steps give the sums of ranks for the two data sets.

1. Put all 25 of the reading scores into L1. In L2 type a 1 next to Rowling scores and a 0 next to Tolstoy scores. You will thus have thirteen 1's followed by twelve 0's in L2.

2. Make a copy of L1 in L3 and a copy of L2 in L5.

3. Press [STAT] [2] to paste "SortA(" then type L3 , L5 [ENTER] to sort the values in L3 and carry along the values in L5.

4. Generate the integers from 1 to 25 in L4 as follows. Type [2nd] [STAT] [▸] [5] to choose the seq option from the LIST<Ops> menu. Type X,X,1,25 and [ENTER]. Next, modify L4, so that it has the ranks of the values in L3 (screen (16)). Make sure to handle the tie in the 9th and 10th values by giving each a rank of $(9+10)/2 = 9.5$.

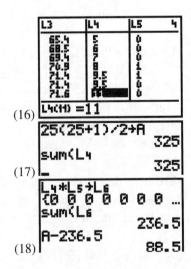
(16)
(17)
(18)

5. Quit and return to the Home screen. Type 25(25+1)/2 [STO▸] [ALPHA] [MATH] [ENTER] for the sum of the 25 ranks which is 325. Find sum(L4) which should also be 325. See screen (17)

6. Multiply L4 by L5 and store in L6 as in screen (18).

7. Find sum(L6) as in screen (18). This is the sum of the Rowling ranks or $236.5 = R$ in the text. The sum of the Tolstoy ranks is found by subtracting this value from the sum of all ranks as in the bottom of screen (18). This value is 88.5.

The above value for R is compared against a value from a normal distribution with mean $n1(n1+n2+1)/2 = 13(13+12+1)/2 = 169$ and standard deviation $\sqrt{(n1*n2*(n1+n2+1)/12}$ $= \sqrt{(13*12*(13+12+1)/12} = 18.385$. The Z-score of this statistic is found by the formula

$Z = \dfrac{R - \mu_R}{\sigma_R} = \dfrac{236.5 - 169}{18.385} = 3.67$. This can all be seen on screen (19).

We find the area in the right tail of the standard normal distribution past Z = 3.67 by pressing $\boxed{2nd}$ $\boxed{VARS}$ $\boxed{2}$ to paste "normalcdf(" then typing 3.67,E99 and pressing $\boxed{ENTER}$. We see the result in screen (20) is .00012. We double for the two tailed test, but we still have a p-value of .00024 which is smaller than the significance level of the test. We have evidence to reject the hypothesis that the distributions for the two samples were the same.

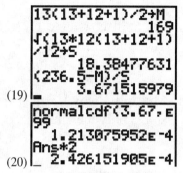

(19)

(20)

KRUSKAL-WALLIS TEST

EXAMPLE Clancy, Rowling, Tolstoy: Data Set 14 in Appendix B contains data obtained from 12 randomly selected pages of each of three different books by the above named authors. Use the Kruskal-Wallis Test to test the null hypothesis that the three samples all came from populations with the same distribution. Use significance level 0.05.

The steps below will explain how to get the sum of the ranks for the data from a specific sample.

1. Place all of the 36 data values in L1. Start with the Clancy values, followed by Rowling and Tolstoy. In L2, place a 1 next to each Clancy value, a 2 next to each Rowling value and a 3 next to each Tolstoy value. Make a copy of L1 in L3.

2. Press $\boxed{STAT}$ $\boxed{2}$ to paste "SortA(" then type L3 , L2 $\boxed{ENTER}$ to sort the values in L3 carrying along L2.

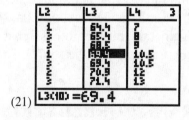

(21)

3. Generate the integers from 1 to 36 in L4 as follows. Type $\boxed{2nd}$ $\boxed{STAT}$ $\boxed{\blacktriangleright}$ $\boxed{5}$ to choose the seq option from the LIST<Ops> menu. Type X,X,1,36 and $\boxed{ENTER}$. Next, modify L4, so that it has the ranks of the values in L3. Make sure to handle the tie at ranks 10 and 11 by giving each the rank (10+11)/2 = 10.5. See screen (21).

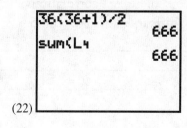

4. Screen (22) shows that the sum of ranks 1 to 36 is 666 and also confirms that the sum of the ranks in L4 is also 666.

(22)

5. Next perform SortA(L2 , L3 , L4 to sort the values in L2 and carry along the values in L3 and L4.

6. In L5, place twelve 1's followed by twenty-four 0's. This places a 1 next to each Clancy data value. Screen (23) shows line 12 of the STAT editor.

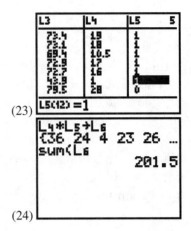

(23)

7. Multiply L4 by L5 and store the results in L6. This stores only the Clancy ranks in L6. Then find sum(L6) to obtain $R_1 = 201.5$. See screen (24)

(24)

Repeat steps 6 and 7 above but with 1 next to the Rowling ranks and 0's next to all others to get R_2 and similarly with Tolstoy and R_3.

Once you have determined that $R_1 = 201.5$, $R_2 = 337$ and $R_3 = 127.5$, you can calculate

the test statistic H by the formula $H = \dfrac{12}{N(N+1)} \left(\dfrac{R_1^2}{n_1} + \dfrac{R_2^2}{n_2} + \dfrac{R_3^2}{n_3} \right) - 3(N+1)$

$$= \dfrac{12}{36(36+1)} \left(\dfrac{201.5^2}{12} + \dfrac{337^2}{12} + \dfrac{127.5^2}{12} \right) - 3(36+1) = 16.949.$$

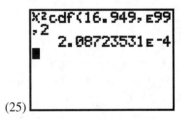

(25)

The distribution of H is chi-squared with k−1 = 3−1 = 2 degrees of freedom. We find the p-value of 16.949 in screen (25) by typing [2nd] [VARS] [7] to paste the χ^2cdf(on the screen. Then type 16.949, E99, 2 and [ENTER]. We find the p-value is 0.0002087. This is certainly less than the significance level of 0.05, so we have evidence against the null hypothesis that the samples came from populations with the same distribution.

RANK CORRELATION

EXAMPLE Perceptions of Beauty: *marie claire* magazine asked men and women to rank the beauty of ten different women. The table below shows the resulting ranks. Test to see if there is a correlation between the rankings given by men and women. Use significance level $\alpha = 0.05$.

Men	4	2	5	1	3	6	7	8	9	10
Women	2	6	7	3	1	10	4	8	5	9

With the data in L1 and L2, the scatter diagram in screen (26) shows little evidence of a relationship between the ranks given by men and women

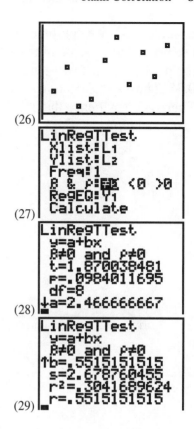

(26)

Press [STAT] [▶] [▶] [ALPHA] [SIN] to choose option E:LinRegTTest from the STAT<Tests> menu. Set up the screen as in screen (27). Highlight Calculate in the bottom line of screen (27), and then press [ENTER] for screens (28) and (29). The last line of screen (29) gives $r_S = 0.552$.

(27)

To test the hypothesis, use the critical value from Table A-9 of the text. Do not use Table A-6 (which was used for the Pearson correlation coefficient) because it requires the populations sampled to be normally distributed.

(28)

The critical value is 0.648 > 0.552, so we fail to reject the null hypothesis. It appears that men and women have different perceptions of beauty.

Note: The t and p-value of screen (28) are for the Pearson correlation coefficient and do not apply for the ranks.

(29)

RUNS TEST FOR RANDOMNESS

EXAMPLE Boston Rainfall on Mondays: Refer to the rainfall amounts for 52 consecutive Mondays in Boston as listed in Data Set 11 of Appendix B and repeated below with 0 representing no rain and 1 representing some rain. Is there sufficient evidence to support the claim that rain on Mondays is not random. Use a 0.05 significance level.

```
0000  1  0  1  00  1  00  1  000  1  00  111  0000
1  0  1  0  111  0  1  000  1  000  1  0  1  00 1 000 1
```

$n_1 = 33$ = the number of zeros or dry days.
$n_2 = 19$ = the number of ones or days with some rain
$G = 30$ = the number of runs or groupings above
Since $n_1 > 20$ we can use formulas given in the text for μ_G and σ_G. Both formulas use only the values for n_1 and n_2. See screens (30) and (31). The test statistic z is computed as $z = (G-\mu_G)/\sigma_G = (30-25.115)/3.306 = 1.48$. See the bottom of screen (31).

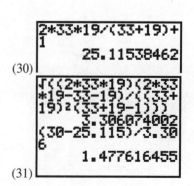

(30)

(31)

In screen (32) we compute the p-value for this test. We use normalcdf(pasted in from [2nd] [VARS] [2]. We double the p-value for the two-tailed test and obtain 0.1389 > 0.05. Thus we fail to reject the null hypothesis.
There is no evidence that rainfall on Mondays in Boston is not random.

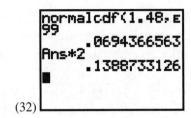

(32)

13   Statistical Process Control

In this chapter we will use the TI-83 Plus to plot run charts and control charts for the range, $\bar{x}$, and proportions.

RUN CHARTS

EXAMPLE   Manufacturing Aircraft Altimeters: Treating the 80 altimeter errors in Table 13-1 of the text as a string of consecutive measurements, construct a run chart using a vertical axis for the errors and a horizontal axis to identify the order of the sample data.

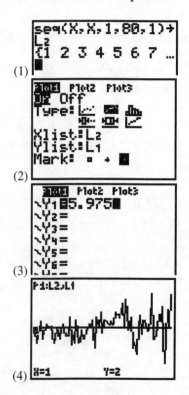

1. Put the 80 data values in list L1. You can use STAT ▶ 1 ENTER to find the overall mean is 5.975.

2. Generate integers from 1 to 80 and store them in L2 with 2nd STAT ▶ 5 (to paste in "seq(" from the LISTS<Ops> menu). Then type X,X,1,80,1).Then press STO▶ 2nd 2 ENTER. See screen (1).

3. Set up Plot1 as an xy-Line plot as in screen (2). All other statplots should be turned off.

4. Press Y= and let Y1 = 5.975. See screen (3).

5. Temporarily turn off the axes by pressing 2nd ZOOM and choosing AxesOff. (Be sure to change this back after you are through with this chapter).

6. Press ZOOM 9 then adjust the Window to better fill the screen by setting Xmin = 0 and Xmax = 80. Then press TRACE for screen (4).

Below is part of Table 13-1 which will be useful in the next two examples.

Day	Mean	Range	Day	Mean	Range	Day	Mean	Range	Day	Mean	Rnnge
1	2.50	19	6	-0.75	26	11	10.75	3	16	9.50	17
2	2.75	13	7	0.00	21	12	12.75	11	17	8.75	10
3	1.00	15	8	0.25	13	13	21.00	13	18	8.25	43
4	0.25	11	9	1.25	26	14	13.00	28	19	12.25	31
5	2.00	11	10	10.50	18	15	3.25	32	20	9.75	63

CONTROL CHART FOR MONITORING VARIATION: THE R CHART

EXAMPLE Manufacturing Aircraft Altimeters: Refer to the altimeter errors in Table 13-1 of the text. Using the samples of size n=4, construct a control chart for R

1. Put the day (integers 1 to 20) in L1 and the corresponding ranges in L2.

2. To find the mean of the data in L2 use [STAT] [▶] [1] [2nd] [2] [ENTER]. You will find $\overline{R}$ = 21.2. You can use this value to find the control limits as in the text. You will find UCL = 48.4 and LCL = 0.

3. Set up Plot 1 as in screen (5).

4. Set up the Y= Editor with the control limits as in screen (6).

5. Press [ZOOM] [9] then press [TRACE] for screen (7) which is similar to the R-chart in the text.

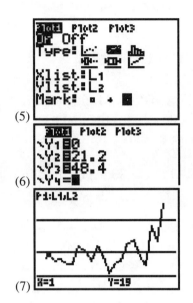

(5)

(6)

(7)

CONTROL CHART FOR MONITORING PROCESS MEAN: THE $\overline{x}$ CHART

EXAMPLE Manufacturing Aircraft Altimeters: Refer to the altimeter errors in Table 13-1 of the text. Using the samples of size n=4, construct a control chart for $\overline{x}$.

1. Put the day (integers 1 to 20) in L1 and the corresponding means in L2.

2. To find the mean of the data in L2 use [STAT] [▶] [1] [2nd] [2] [ENTER]. You will find $\overline{\overline{x}}$ = 6.45. You can use this value and that of $\overline{R}$ (found above) to find the control limits as in the text. You will find UCL = 21.9 and LCL = −9.0.

3. Set up Plot 1 as in screen (5) above.

4. Set up the Y= Editor with the control limits as in screen (8).

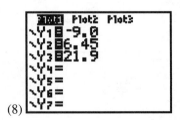

(8)

5. Press ZOOM 9. Change the Window so that the LCL is visible. Try using Ymin = −15. Then press TRACE for screen (9) which is similar to the $\bar{x}$-chart in the text.

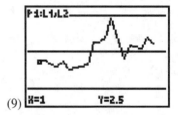

(9)

CONTROL CHART FOR ATTRIBUTES: THE P-CHART

EXAMPLE Deaths from Infectious Diseases: In each of 13 consecutive and recent years, 100,000 subjects were randomly selected and the number who died from respiratory tract infections was recorded, with the results given below. Construct a control chart for p with the control limits as calculated in the text: UCL = 0.000449, CL = 0.000288 and LCL = 0.000127.

25 24 22 25 27 30 31 30 33 32 33 32 31

1. Put the year in L1 (integers from 1 to 13) and the corresponding number of deaths in L2.

2. On the Home screen, type L2 / 100000 and store in L2. See screen (10). This will store the proportion of deaths in L2.

3. Set up Plot 1 as in screen (5) on the preceding page.

4. Set up the Y= editor with the control limits as in screen (11).These limits were calculated in the text to be UCL = 0.000449, CL = 0.000288, and LCL = 0.000127.

5. Press ZOOM 9. Then set the Window so the LCL and UCL are visible. Try Ymin = 0.00009 and Ymax = 0.0005. Then press TRACE for screen (12) which looks very similar to the p chart in the text.

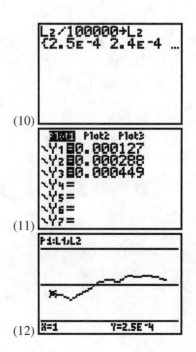

(10)

(11)

(12)

Appendix

Loading the Data Apps, Data, Groups, and Programs from a Computer or Another TI-83 Plus.

This appendix contains information on transferring data and programs from the CD-ROM that came with your main text and is available from the publisher. Also, we give instruction on how to install a data set from the data Apps and how to make and install your own group.

The CD-ROM contains the data sets (except Data Set 4) from Appendix B of *Elementary Statistics* (9th Edition) by Mario F. Triola. For the TI-83 Plus, data is given in an Apps (or application) called TRIOLA9e APP. For the TI-83, data is given as individual lists in ASCII format as text files (with extensions of .txt). The CD-ROM also contains two programs A1ANOVA.83p (used in Chapter11) and A2MULREG.83p (used in Chapter 9).

Your instructor will probably load the data (and programs, if needed) onto your TI-83 Plus, or you can transfer them from the CD-ROM with your computer if you have the TI-GRAPH LINK software and cable available from Texas Instruments. See the guidebook that comes with the TI-83 Plus for information on the TI-GRAPH LINK.

Loading Data or Programs from One TI-83 Plus to Another

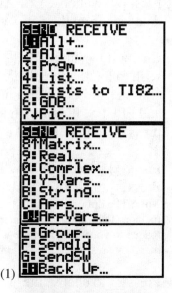

1. Connect one TI-83 Plus to another with the cable that came with the calculator. The link port is located at the center of the bottom edge of the calculator.

2. On the TI-83 Plus which is to <u>receive</u> the data or program, press [2nd] [X,T,Θ,n] (to choose the LINK menu as seen in Screen (1)). Press [▶] to highlight RECEIVE. Press [ENTER] or [1] and see the message "Waiting" displayed.

3. On the TI-83 Plus that is to <u>send</u> the program or data, press [2nd] [X,T,Θ,n]. Cursor down the list. When what you wish to send is highlighted, press [ENTER]. In this example we are sending choice C: Apps, but we could send a program or a list of data with options 3 and 4. Once we enter on choice C: Apps, we use [▼] to point out TRIOLA9e APP and press [ENTER] for screen (2).

(1)

(2)

4. Press ▶ to highlight TRANSMIT. Press ENTER or 1 to transmit whatever you have chosen on the previous step.
   Note: If you are transmitting an App the receiving calculator will signal "garbage collecting" then "receiving", and then "validating" before indicating "Done", so be patient.

   If the name of whatever is being sent is already in use on the receiving calculator that calculator will show a screen like (3). You can then choose to overwrite the old with the new or to rename so you can keep both.

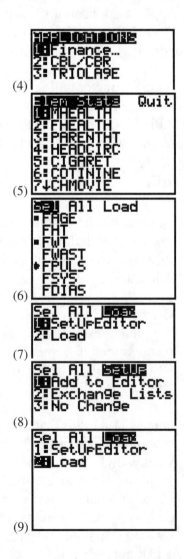

(3)

Using the Data Apps (For TI-83 Plus only)

1. Press the APPS key for a screen like screen (4).
   Note: We assume that TRIOLA9e App has been installed in this example. The list of other Apps available may vary.

   (4)

2. Use ▼ to highlight the number in from of TRIOLA9e. Then press ENTER for a title screen that soon changes to screen (5) which contains a list of the data sets in Appendix B of your text.

   (5)

3. Press 2 to choose FHEALTH and see a list of the data lists from the data set Fhealth. See screen (6).

   (6)

4. Cursor down and press ENTER next to each list you wish to load. A small black square will designate a chosen list. For our example we choose FAGE, FWT and FPULS. If you wish to load all lists in a set then press ▶ to highlight "All".

   (7)

5. Press ▶ ▶ to highlight "Load" as in screen (7). Press 1 to choose "SetUpEditor" and see screen (8).
   Note: The option 2:Load loads the lists from archive memory to random access memory. The data would not be loaded to your Stats Editor but would be available on the Lists menu by pressing 2nd STAT. See page 8 screen (20).

   (8)

6. Press 2 to choose the "Exchange Lists" option and see screen (9).
   Note: Option 1 will add the lists to the lists already in the Stats Editor. Option 3 will not change the editor and place the lists in the Lists menu as described in the Note with Step 5.

   (9)

7. Press ② to choose "Load" and screen (10) informs you that the List(s) have been loaded. Pressing any key returns to screen (5) and pressing ②nd MODE lets you Quit and return to the Home screen.

8. To see the results of our work, press STAT ① to check out the Stat Editor. In screen (11) we see the lists we loaded are in fact there ready for us to use.

Grouping and Ungrouping (For TI-83 Plus only)

Just as the Data Apps has lists of data from the text grouped together, you may want to group lists of data and/or matrices and/or programs. The advantage to doing this is that groups are saved in Archive memory and do not take up room in RAM until you want to use them.

Example Group the data sets FAGE, FWT, and FPULS just moved in from the Apps in the preceding example into a group called FEM. (These data are already part of the group FHEALTH in the TRIOLA9e App, so we are just doing this to provide an example.)

1. Press ②nd + to choose the MEM menu. Then choose option 8: Group and see screen (12). Press ENTER for the first part of screen (13). Then type the name of the group "FEM" to duplicate screen (13).

2. Press ENTER for screen (14) and then press ④ to choose "List" and see a screen like (15). Cursor down the menu of lists and press ENTER next to each list which you wish to include in the group FEM. Again, chosen lists will be designated by little black squares in the left margin.

3. Press ▶ to highlight "Done". Then press ENTER for screen (16).

Note: Now if you delete the three lists from RAM they will still be in archive memory. To return them to RAM, return to screen (12) and highlight "Ungroup" and press ENTER. You would then select group FEM to ungroup. Even though the list will then reside in RAM, it will remain in archive memory unless it is deleted as a Group similar to what was done on page 7 for lists.

INDEX

TI-83 Plus Quick Reference

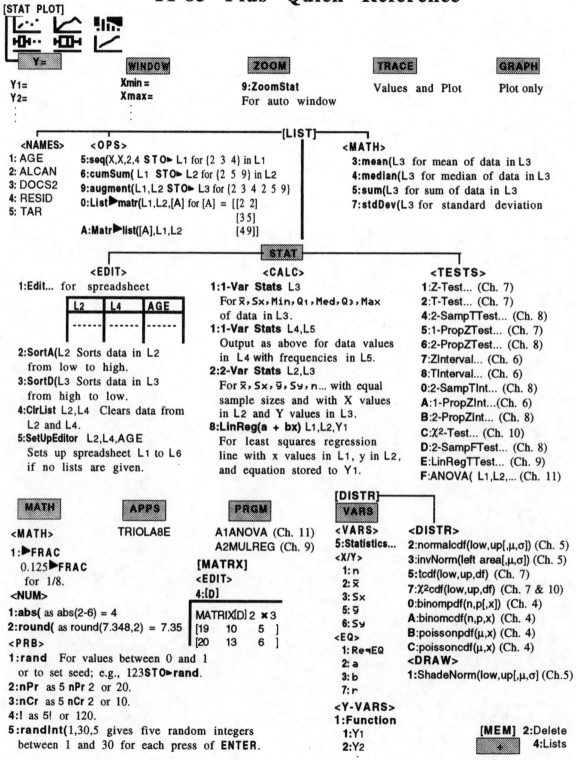

[STAT PLOT]

Y=

Y1=
Y2=

WINDOW

Xmin =
Xmax=

ZOOM

9:ZoomStat
For auto window

TRACE

Values and Plot

GRAPH

Plot only

[LIST]

<NAMES>
1: AGE
2: ALCAN
3: DOCS2
4: RESID
5: TAR

<OPS>
5:seq(X,X,2,4 STO► L1 for {2 3 4} in L1
6:cumSum(L1 STO► L2 for {2 5 9} in L2
9:augment(L1,L2 STO► L3 for {2 3 4 2 5 9}
0:List►matr(L1,L2,[A] for [A] = [[2 2]
                              [3 5]
A:Matr►list([A],L1,L2   [4 9]]

<MATH>
3:mean(L3 for mean of data in L3
4:median(L3 for median of data in L3
5:sum(L3 for sum of data in L3
7:stdDev(L3 for standard deviation

STAT

<EDIT>
1:Edit... for spreadsheet

L2	L4	AGE
------	------	------

2:SortA(L2 Sorts data in L2 from low to high.
3:SortD(L3 Sorts data in L3 from high to low.
4:ClrList L2,L4 Clears data from L2 and L4.
5:SetUpEditor L2,L4,AGE
Sets up spreadsheet L1 to L6 if no lists are given.

<CALC>
1:1-Var Stats L3
For $\bar{x}$, Sx, Min, Q1, Med, Q3, Max of data in L3.
1:1-Var Stats L4,L5
Output as above for data values in L4 with frequencies in L5.
2:2-Var Stats L2,L3
For $\bar{x}$, Sx, $\bar{y}$, Sy, n... with equal sample sizes and with X values in L2 and Y values in L3.
8:LinReg(a + bx) L1,L2,Y1
For least squares regression line with x values in L1, y in L2, and equation stored to Y1.

<TESTS>
1:Z-Test... (Ch. 7)
2:T-Test... (Ch. 7)
4:2-SampTTest... (Ch. 8)
5:1-PropZTest... (Ch. 7)
6:2-PropZTest... (Ch. 8)
7:ZInterval... (Ch. 6)
8:TInterval... (Ch. 6)
0:2-SampTInt... (Ch. 8)
A:1-PropZInt...(Ch. 6)
B:2-PropZInt... (Ch. 8)
C:χ^2-Test... (Ch. 10)
D:2-SampFTest... (Ch. 8)
E:LinRegTTest... (Ch. 9)
F:ANOVA(L1,L2,... (Ch. 11)

MATH

<MATH>
1:►FRAC
0.125►FRAC
for 1/8.
<NUM>
1:abs(as abs(2-6) = 4
2:round(as round(7.348,2) = 7.35
<PRB>
1:rand For values between 0 and 1 or to set seed; e.g., 123STO►rand.
2:nPr as 5 nPr 2 or 20.
3:nCr as 5 nCr 2 or 10.
4:! as 5! or 120.
5:randInt(1,30,5 gives five random integers between 1 and 30 for each press of **ENTER**.

APPS

TRIOLA8E

PRGM

A1ANOVA (Ch. 11)
A2MULREG (Ch. 9)

[MATRX]
<EDIT>
4:[D]

MATRIX[D] 2 × 3		
[19	10	5]
[20	13	6]

[DISTR]
VARS

<VARS>
5:Statistics...
<X/Y>
1: n
2: $\bar{x}$
3: Sx
5: $\bar{y}$
6: Sy
<EQ>
1: Re◄EQ
2: a
3: b
7: r
<Y-VARS>
1:Function
1:Y1
2:Y2

<DISTR>
2:normalcdf(low,up[,μ,σ]) (Ch. 5)
3:invNorm(left area[,μ,σ]) (Ch. 5)
5:tcdf(low,up,df) (Ch. 7)
7:χ^2cdf(low,up,df) (Ch. 7 & 10)
0:binompdf(n,p[,x]) (Ch. 4)
A:binomcdf(n,p,x) (Ch. 4)
B:poissonpdf(μ,x) (Ch. 4)
C:poissoncdf(μ,x) (Ch. 4)
<DRAW>
1:ShadeNorm(low,up[,μ,σ]) (Ch.5)

[MEM] 2:Delete
4:Lists